A Guide to MATHEMATICS

for the Intelligent Nonmathematician

by **Edmund C. Berkeley**

Simon and Schuster NEW YORK

CONTENTS

Preface

Part One: **A Way In**

1. *The Iceberg Mathematics*   21

2. *The Hidden Seeds*   32

13. *Integrals—(Continued)*

14. *Equations*   194

15. *Angles*   208

16. *Logic: Properties and Relations*   224

Appendices

The Subject, Purpose, and Method of This Book

THE SUBJECT of this book is mathematics. But unlike many other books about mathematics, its purpose is to be a guide to mathematics expressed in terms of ideas that are familiar to the ordinary intelligent person who is *not* a mathematician. For intelligent people may be divided into two kinds: those who like mathematics; and those who do not care for mathematics, who have found their contacts with it not very interesting and not very congenial. It is the second kind of person for whom this book is written—you, my imagined reader.

In order to be a satisfactory guide to mathematics for *you*, this book needs to deal with many natural, practical questions, like "What is mathematics, really?" and "Can mathematics be useful to me?" and "How can I learn some mathematics?" and "What are the parts of mathematics that are important, and the parts that are not important?" and many more. And the answers to these questions need to be phrased in ways which may be fully understood by an intelligent person who has not in the past been attracted toward mathematics.

There are three main propositions which I seek to demonstrate to you in this book:

A MATHEMATICIAN UNCONSCIOUSLY: The first of these propositions is that without your being fully aware of it you are already a mathematician, and rather a good one too. In fact, you already deal every day with mathematical ideas and deal with them rather well. This thesis is argued in Chapter 2, "The Hidden Seeds," which refers to the seeds of mathematics that can be found hidden in many places in ordinary language.

IMPORTANT MATHEMATICAL IDEAS: The second of these propositions is that there exist some mathematical ideas which are powerful, interesting, useful, and basically simple. Therefore it is worth devoting to them a reasonable amount of reading, studying, and experimenting. Then you can use these important ideas, think with them, and apply them in your own life and affairs. The main body of the book is devoted to making a dozen important mathematical ideas clear and understandable.

THE PROCESS OF UNDERSTANDING: There is also a third main proposition—that it is quite possible for you (or anyone) to understand these ideas (and of course many other ideas), given some time, some interest, and the right technique for understanding. This technique is basic and essentially simple. And so it just is not true that a given (intelligent) person cannot understand a given (rational) idea, under suitable conditions. This thesis is argued in Chapter 3, "Understanding Mathematics."

The Idea of the Mathematical Shape of the Earth

For an example of an important mathematical idea that affects everybody, let's consider the idea of mathematical shape, flat or round, as applied to the earth. In the 1300's and earlier, most people thought that the earth was flat, like a sheet of paper, and that therefore it had an edge, and that if you went too close to the edge, you might fall off. Nowadays, almost all people think that the earth is round, like a ball or sphere (although I have heard rumors of an association of people, called, I believe, the Flat-Earthists, who do not agree), and therefore the earth has no edge, and so no matter where you go on the earth you will not fall off—you will always fall toward the center of the sphere. In other words, a person's idea of the mathematical shape of the earth has a profound effect on his confidence about traveling over the earth.

The Idea of Mathematical Chance

Let's take another example of an important mathematical idea: the idea of mathematical chance. Suppose you are in Las Vegas, Nevada, where gambling is legal. Would you gamble? It is a well-known fact that all gambling games are in the long run profitable to the casino which offers them. Indeed, if this were not true, casinos could not stay in business. Also, it is mathematically predictable that every person, without exception, who plays in a casino will in the long run lose all the money that he risks; in the long run he does not even have a chance of breaking even! But the casinos in Las Vegas continue to draw a great many customers who either have been unable to accept this mathematical idea or have never been aware of it—and the customers inexorably lose their money.

The Usual Presentation of Mathematics

The intelligent nonmathematician—very sensibly and very properly—has had some justified complaints about the way in which mathematics has usually been presented to him. Often this way of presentation has in the past been wrapped around with a cloak of authority, with an air of intellectual snobbishness, often with an emphasis of "do thus and thus—never mind if you don't understand." This emphasis has been strong in arithmetic. There have been other barriers besides (they are discussed in Chapter 1). The psychological effects of these barriers have been considerable and unfortunate, and they are hard to overcome.

Other Presentations

There are other ways, though, of presenting mathematics. One of these is to give clear and simple answers to the nonmathematician's basic questions, to perceive imaginatively what else he needs from where he sits, to give many examples, and to use for explanation, as much as possible, the words and ideas of the common everyday world. This is the method we try to use in this book.

Another way may be the "new" mathematics, which is being taught in a number of elementary and secondary schools, under the leadership of some groups of scholars such as those at the University of Illinois ("Illinois math"). We shall have more to say about that in Chapter 21.

How to Read This Book

In reading this book, and obtaining ideas from it, please do not think that you have to start at the beginning and read all the way through systematically. Instead, plan to browse as if you were in a bookstore. Many of the chapters are fairly independent units. In fact, if you read systematically, you will find some evident repetition; sometimes exactly the same unfamiliar idea is explained again at another place because the idea needs to be understood at that place also.

If you find a chapter a bit troublesome to absorb all at once, skip to the next chapter and come back to the troublesome place some other time, when you may be more ready to try to understand it. Sometimes understanding an idea well includes getting used to it—and this is a process which may take days or weeks or months.

Criticisms and Corrections

This book began in 1948. Now, 18 years later, and many thousands of words changed and changed and changed again, this book is going to press. But it does not seem really finished: so many possibilities for improvement in this presentation can still be seen.

If you, my reader, find an opportunity as you read this book to note what you find obscure or missing or superfluous, and then write and tell me, I shall be very grateful. Your suggestions, comments, and criticisms, will be most useful to make the next edition better and to help open an inviting pathway to mathematics for more people.

It is too much to hope that there are no errors in this book. I shall be grateful also to every reader who catches the errors and sends me corrections.

Edmund C. Berkeley

Newtonville, Massachusetts 02160
September 1, 1966

Part One

A WAY IN

The Iceberg Mathematics

MATHEMATICS IS LIKE AN ICEBERG, a small part above
water and visible, nine times as much below water and in-
visible. Most of us have seen only a little bit of mathematics
under rather chilly conditions; it has been hard for us to
form a good idea of the submerged part. In fact, our view of
mathematics has been like the view we would have as a
passenger on the deck of an ocean liner off the tip of New-
foundland in early June, when in faint sunlight through cold
mist a sailor speaks to us, points, and says, "There is an iceberg." "Oh!" we say, looking at it, and we think hopefully
of the next day when we will be beyond the iceberg area.
We are sure that the best thing to do about most icebergs is
to go the opposite way, calmly leaving the iceberg in posses-
sion of whatever it has.

And yet mathematics is no longer a subject which intelligent people who are not mathematicians can easily leave
alone. It is becoming too important for the understanding of
industry, business, science, and many other human activities, as well as for their guidance and operation. In 1945 the
explosion of an atomic bomb made reality out of Albert
Einstein's famous mathematical equation E equals M C
squared (it makes no difference at this point just what that

21

somewhat mystical phrase may mean); and ever since, non-mathematical people everywhere have needed to know more than they do about mathematics.

How do we start?

Whenever we come to a subject that is not familiar to us — and mathematics is not familiar to many of us — we are likely to have three things we need to do at the start:

- we need to find out what the subject is really about;
- we need to correct any misimpressions that we may have previously had; and
- we need to satisfy ourselves that it makes sense for us to be interested in it.

Let us try to do these three things for mathematics.

What Is Mathematics Really About?

It is hard to say all that mathematics is, but it is fairly easy to say what mathematics is about.

It deals mainly with:

- numbers, like 2, minus 10, $3\frac{1}{2}$, .605, and so on;
- shapes, like a circle or a straight line or a globe;
- sizes, measurements, and comparisons like "big," "more," "as long as";
- arrangements, like "between" or like the six possible sequences of the letters N, T, A;
- patterns and models, like the pattern of branches on a tree or a model of a snow crystal;
- order, like "second," "next," "one by one";
- change, variation, and graphs, as in "The temperature will be in the high 80's this afternoon but in the low 60's tonight — let me show you a graph of the expected temperature";
- chances and risks, such as are referred to in words like "probably," "maybe."

In addition, mathematics includes *calculation* — exact, logical processes by means of which anyone who knows the processes can pass correctly from some numbers (or other data) given at the start of a problem to numbers (or other data) that one desires to know at the end of working on the problem. In essence, the form of any calculation is like the form of an income tax return: it contains a set of spaces or boxes in which you put certain numbers (or other data) as called for; and as you proceed from one box to another, you may have to carry out some operations on the numbers (or other data), such as selecting which one is the larger, or which one begins with the earlier letters of the alphabet, etc.

What Kind of Thing Is Mathematics?

Part of the reason why mathematics puzzles nonmathematicians is that it is hard for a nonmathematician to decide what kind of thing mathematics is. Is it a science? Is it an art? Is it a language? In fact, mathematics is all three.

We might say that mathematics is preeminently: the science of what is general; the art of deducing; and the language that calculates. Let's explain that.

More explicitly, among all the existing sciences, mathematics is clearly the most general science, the science which is least restricted to any one particular area of the world, real or imagined. This is because mathematics deals or can deal with any objects or observations whatever, whether real or imaginary. Numbers can count atoms or stars, motor cars or people, angels or devils. A sequence of numbers can specify the sequence of stations on a railroad, or the sequence of days in a year, or the sequence of points in an argument. Almost no other science is as general as mathematics.

Among all the arts, mathematics (together with logic, which some people consider part of mathematics) is the art of skillfully reasoning from some statements that are assumed to be true, to other statements that must inevitably follow from them. For example, from two plus three equals five, and some other statements, it follows that 222 plus 333 equals 555. No other art (except logic) is the art of skillfully and correctly deducing.

Finally, among all the languages, mathematics is a calculating language, where any idea whatever can be named and discussed, analyzed and calculated with (dealt with in exact reasoning processes). The mathematician says, "Let x stand for . . . . Then . . . ." And by and by, as Alfred North Whitehead remarked, the mathematician has "weighed the stars and counted the billions of molecules in a drop of water." No other language to an equal degree frees a person to make words or symbols for any idea he chooses, only requiring of him to show that he can calculate, carry through useful, precise deductions with these words or symbols.

One might at first think that all calculation is contained in mathematics. But this is not true. A lot of calculation takes place in ordinary language. For example, removing ambiguity from sentences to make them clear is part of calculation: in "John put Robert's hat on his head," does "his" refer to John or Robert? The grammatical rule says "Robert," but isn't it unusual for a person to put a hat on someone else's head? The relative portion of ordinary language used for calculation, however, is minor; the language that makes a specialty of elaborate calculation is mathematics.

Some people have found out what mathematics is about, and what kind of thing it is, and have themselves taken hold in one way or another of a significant part of the great power that mathematics contains. To these people there is no finer or more exciting instrument of the human mind than mathematics.

But we cannot say that most people have understood this. Education in mathematics up to now has not spread widely this degree of understanding of "What is mathematics?"

Why not?

Barriers to Mathematics:
Our Inevitable Introduction to Mathematical Ideas

The first part of our trouble in understanding mathematics is inevitable: it is the introduction to mathematical ideas which we experience as we grow up.

The usual introduction—and it is a necessary and natural introduction—to mathematics is numbers and arithmetic. About the age of two or two and a half, a child acquires a clear idea of two: one hand, the other hand, both hands, two hands. Some time later come the ideas of three, one, and many. Ideas of four, five, six, and seven seem not to be reached until the child can count. And more and more of the ideas of arithmetic can only be acquired as the child learns processes—at home, in kindergarten, and in the first grades. Yet these ideas still have very little meaning to him.

Our introduction to mathematical ideas of necessity begins when we do not know very much, nor can we know very much. And our introduction continues over many years, usually at least 12 or 14 years, in bits and pieces and with many interruptions and ordeals, such as trying to pass tests and answer questions when we don't understand very well. And so it often happens that we do not see the forest because of the trees—we are not able to see the nature of mathematics, because we have been too occupied with the details. Only when we reach the age of reflection are we really prepared to understand mathematics.

Barrier: **Our Readiness or Unreadiness**

The second part of the difficulty of most of us with mathematics results from the untidy, irregular development of readiness or maturity. A child six months old cannot walk, no matter how carefully he may be taught to walk. Physically he is not mature enough to walk. Yet most children a year and a half old are walking. This has happened whether or not they have been "taught"—they have become physically ready and mature enough to walk, and they fall into the technique of walking quite easily.

In the same way, with mathematics, the time when one is ready or mature enough to understand a mathematical idea and the time when that idea is usually taught in school may be far apart. Some people take much more time than others to reach the same level of readiness to absorb certain kinds of mathematical ideas.

What Is the Biggest Number?

A parent who likes to teach sometimes supplements the work of the classroom teacher and seizes the arrival of readiness. He waits and watches for certain questions arising in the mind of his child, or stimulates them through questions when the child seems to be ready and interested. For example:

PARENT: "Can you tell me what is the biggest number?"
CHILD: "A million."
PARENT: "Can you think of a number bigger than a million?"
CHILD: "Yes, two million."
PARENT: "What would be bigger than two million?"
CHILD: "A million million."
PARENT: "What is bigger than that?"
CHILD (after pausing): "Is there any biggest number?"
PARENT: "No, there actually is no biggest number."
CHILD: "Why not?"
PARENT: "This is why: because as soon as you or I or anyone says a big number, some one else can say a bigger number still."
CHILD: "Oh!"

You can hear a person change his mind, absorb something new, when he says that "Oh!"

But it is difficult to make this kind of conversation happen at the right time. Most of us have not benefited from this kind of challenging series of questions and explanation at the right time.

Barrier: The Chores of Mathematics

The road to mathematics is not only rough with impediments, but also along the path there are lions chained. And by their loud roaring, many of us are frightened away.

One of the lions is the chores of mathematics. Learning the addition table (with its elementary addition facts, like nine and six are 15) is a chore. Learning the multiplication table (with its elementary multiplication facts, like seven times eight is 56) is a chore. And in order to do arithmetic properly these chores, and many more, have to be learned and learned solidly and for a lifetime. And like all chores, if we procrastinate before starting and dawdle while doing them, they take much longer than they need to take, and they leave a bad taste in our mouth and a bad recollection in our memory.

It is hardly possible for us to come near to using the powers of mathematics until we have emotionally accepted the chores and learned them, and gained some satisfaction from doing them well. The chores have to be done, and done well; and after that we have acquired the training and background for the enjoyment of mathematics.

Barrier: Authority and Rebellion

Another important barrier to learning mathematics is, as was mentioned earlier, the tendency of teachers to present mathematics (and particularly arithmetic) with a strong dose of authority: "Do thus and thus—never mind if you don't understand completely."

In fact, on some occasions they may have some good

arguments on their side. For example, many of the conventions and procedures of mathematics are arbitrary—in the sense that other conventions and procedures would do just as well. For example, let us consider two methods for subtracting, as illustrated in subtracting 369 from 517:

$$\begin{array}{r} 517 \\ \underline{369} \\ 148 \end{array}$$

By the method I learned in school a long time ago, I say under my breath:

"9 from 7 won't go, borrow 10, 10 and 7 is 17, 9 from 17 is 8, put down 8, and go to the next column; ADD the borrowed 1 to 6, it makes 7, 7 from 1 won't go, borrow 10, 10 and 1 is 11, 7 from 11 is 4, put down the 4 and go to the next column; ADD the borrowed 1 to the 3; it makes 4, 4 from 5 is 1, put down 1; the answer is 148."

But there is another method. Somebody else might say under his breath:

"9 from 7 won't go, borrow 10, 10 and 7 is 17, 9 from 17 is 8, put down the 8, and go to the next column; SINCE 1 is borrowed, subtract 1 from 1 making 0, 6 from 0 won't go, borrow 10, 10 and 0 is 10, 6 from 10 is 4, put down the 4, and go to the next column; SINCE 1 is borrowed, subtract 1 from 5 making 4, 3 from 4 is 1, put down the 1; the answer is 148."

Both methods are right—and different. I prefer mine; other people will prefer theirs. But a teacher will need to choose one method arbitrarily and teach that, saying, "This is the choice I have made, and this is the way we will do it."

Yet the argument from authority is not nearly as sound as the argument from good reasons; and the repeated exercise of authority is likely to produce irritation and lead to rebellion. Also, when a student understands the reason for a decision, he is much better off in the long run, because if the reason changes, he is prepared to change the decision. For example:

STUDENT: "Why use the sign × for 'times' meaning multiply?"

TEACHER: "It is an arbitrary choice; it has been used for a long time."

STUDENT: "It can easily be confused with the letter X."

TEACHER: "That is true, and often troublesome."

STUDENT: "Why not use some other sign, perhaps an asterisk [*]?"

TEACHER: "An asterisk could be used. As a matter of fact, in some present-day languages for instructing computers an asterisk [*] and not × is used for multiplication. The sign asterisk would be a reasonable choice in many places."

Barrier: **Cultural Attitudes**

Another important barrier to mathematics is to be found in present-day culture in the United States. Much antagonism exists in school and in the community toward a "highbrow," an "egghead," a "brain," a "teacher's pet." Among the uncles and aunts you know, it is likely that at least someone will say, "Oh, I was never able to understand mathematics, and it has never bothered me in the least."

A student regularly wins the school letter for prowess in football, but a student does not regularly win it for high distinction in mathematics. Instead, other students will say about him, "Does a guy like that get any fun out of life?" Among students in many schools, it is usually considered respectable to get average marks, but clearly disloyal to the crowd to get excellent marks.

So, before an intelligent young person can dare to learn mathematics well, and be happy to get A in his marks, he needs to develop a strength to be different from most of the other students. He needs an inner resourcefulness, a capacity to be guided by other standards than those common in the group of young people around him. And for most of us, when we are in school, this is not appealing.

Is It Sensible for Me to Be Interested in Mathematics?

And yet, in spite of the misimpressions that we may have about mathematics, and the barriers to understanding it that may have been in our way in the past, when we reach the age of reflection, we are likely to say to ourselves, "Perhaps there is something for me after all in mathematics. Perhaps there is something in it important for me."

Nowadays is a good time to become interested in mathematics. Mathematicians are no longer assigned to third-floor rooms in college departments. Instead they are sought after by business and industry, given positions of importance, titles like "Operations Research Analyst," or "Management Consultant" or "Systems Evaluator," and are paid adequate salaries, whether in business or elsewhere. Mathematicians are being particularly aided by the "computer revolution," the advent of machines which can carry out more than 100,000 arithmetical and logical operations per second in long sequences of reasonable operations. In this way the "dirty work" of arithmetic in huge quantities is done by obedient and swift electronic slaves. Many topics of mathematics are becoming prominent in the press: newspapers publish graphs; *The New York Times* now and then even publishes equations. In countless places, in our complicated modern society, figures are dug out and are then used to make decisions with. For example, a school committee must continually watch figures of births, immigration, and emigration in its community, so as to have appropriate space for children in its schools. The more important ideas of mathematics (the ideas of mathematics are by no means all equally important) are having a more and more profound influence on countless facets of our society.

So it is sensible for nonmathematical people to become interested in the important ideas of mathematics.

Can Mathematics Actually Be Useful to Me?

Some parts of mathematics can be useful to any intelligent person. They help him make better decisions. They enable him to see the structure of the world more clearly. They affect his common activities. Here is a partial list of common human activities in which basic mathematical ideas (many of them explained in this book) can be useful to any intelligent person:

reading graphs and using tables
applying formulas
estimating
taking samples
making models and diagrams
determining chances
predicting the future
making decisions

Graphs and tables summarize a lot of information; to be able to read a graph or a table makes the information accessible. Estimating is the technique of making good rough guesses about numbers. Models, plans, schemes, maps, diagrams are representations or pictures of the real world. In all these activities, the results obtained with some appropriate mathematical reasoning are better than the results obtained without.

But you may say: "This is all very fine, but how much effort do I have to make? How much work do I have to do?"

To try to answer your question, it seems to me that, with the technique for understanding explained in this book, you can find out a good deal about many important, interesting, and entertaining ideas of mathematics, in exchange for not very much effort. In fact, on the basis of the method of presentation in this book, I would estimate that more than a dozen important ideas of mathematics could become tools for you to use, with less than a dozen hours of reading and reflecting.

The Hidden Seeds

2

The Seeds of Mathematics Hidden in Ordinary Language

One good way to approach mathematics is to notice the quantity of useful and important mathematical ideas that are expressed in ordinary language and have become familiar everyday tools. These ideas are, in fact, so much a part of our ordinary thinking that we hardly ever notice their true mathematical nature. Like planted seeds, hidden because they are covered with earth, these ideas are seeds of mathematics hidden in the surroundings of ordinary, everyday language.

The Unconscious Use of Common Mathematical Ideas

Let us suppose for a moment that you are one of a commonly occurring kind of human being: a person who is intelligent and who is not a mathematician. You do a fair amount of reading. You try to keep up with the news. You do keep up with your work. You have no great concern with mathematics; you think of it as something remote from you, something to be avoided when it crops up. Except for some

32

occasional contacts, such as adding bills, and calculating income taxes, you avoid contacts with mathematics. You may say to yourself, "I am not a mathematician. It's over my head."

Yet you are a mathematician and a good practical one at that. In almost all the sentences that you say, in almost all the thoughts that you think, you make use of ideas that are really and essentially mathematical. In fact, you have had a lot of experience with many important mathematical ideas, and you can use them correctly nearly all the time—although it is quite likely that you are not conscious of this fact in the least.

How can this last assertion be true? Well, suppose we check it by reading over the last two paragraphs just above, and making a list of all the basic ideas in them that belong essentially to mathematics. (We shall leave out words that deal with the subject matter of the paragraphs, like "mathematician" and "calculating.") By an idea belonging to mathematics I mean that the study of that idea in precise detail is carried out by the science of mathematics.

In those last two paragraphs we can count more than 20 different mathematical ideas which are in common everyday use, and yet which are not conspicuous at all, which are hidden. These ideas are shown in the list below.

a	not
one	and
commonly occurring	no
a fair amount	remote from
almost all, nearly all	except
-s (for plural)	in
a lot of	very
the least	kind
many	keep up with
great	such as
is, are	

You may say, "Are these really mathematical ideas?" Yes, they are. The "-s" for plural, which is the distinction between "bill" and "bills," between "sentence" and "sentences," between "thought" and "thoughts," is the distinction between singular and plural, the distinction between one and more than one—and the study of this distinction belongs to mathematics, the part which is arithmetical counting. The detailed study of the gradations between "none," "a few," "many," "almost all," "all" belongs to mathematics—the arithmetic of proportional measurements. The distinction between "in" and "out" belongs to mathematics—a branch of mathematics called "topology," from "topos," a Greek word for "place," and "-logy" meaning "science," that is to say, the scientific study of place and related ideas. The detailed study of "is," "not," "and," "except," and a number of similar ideas, belongs in a branch of mathematics called "Boolean algebra," named after a great English mathematician, George Boole, who laid out most of this algebra in his book *The Laws of Thought*, published in 1854. And so on, for all the other words mentioned in the above list.

You may say:

> But what about other uses of "in"? In the phrase "interested in the world," we have to use "in" and we can't say "out of." "Interested out of the world" would be nonsense. And so what has happened here to the so-called mathematical distinction between "in" and "out of"?

Actually, the word "in," like many other words with a basic mathematical meaning, often furnishes useful extended senses, where the original mathematical meaning is rather thinned out. This is an advantage, not a disadvantage. Mathematical words, like words from other sciences, may be highly useful in their extended senses, because the basic meaning can be clearly applied in many contexts.

Common Everyday Words with Mathematical Meaning: Place or Space

From your previous experience you might think that the mathematical ideas most commonly used in ordinary language are numbers and other numerical ideas. But this is not true. The most commonly used, the most unavoidable mathematical ideas are the ideas dealing with place — location, region, and direction — space.

By examining vocabularies of common words, we can put down the following list of the commonest words (and therefore the commonest ideas) that deal with place.

Location	Region	Direction
at	top	to
before, ahead of	bottom	from
behind, beyond	left	up
over, above	right	down
under, below,	front	along
underneath	back	across
in, inside of	center	through
out, out of, outside of	side	into
on	edge	out of
off	corner	onto
against	end	forward
around, near, beside,	middle	backward
next	neighborhood,	sideways
touching	surrounding	toward
opposite to		away
between, among		way

Suppose we should want to be more specific about location, or region, or direction, than we are allowed to by these words, and by combinations of them in phrases such as "between the top and the middle." Then at once we find we have to become considerably more technical: we would need to measure distances and angles, use numbers, and report measurements. So the words listed above clearly meet one of the tests for a word belonging to mathematics: if we want to be any more specific, we have to be a good deal more technical, and the technique we use is mathematics.

Shape or Form

The next group of short, common, everyday words that belong to mathematics are the words having to do with shape or form:

flat, plane, surface	hole
round, circle, ball, globe	bump, bulge, knob;
point, dot	stick up, project
line, straight line	cover, covering
curve, curved line	crack
fork, bend, angle, turn	fold
square, block	knot
space, spacing	hanging
loop, ring, oval, coil, bowl, hollow	lump, block, chunk, solid

Thinking over the words used to specify shape, we may be reminded that we often use phrases such as "needle-shaped," "rod-shaped," "like a pear," "like an egg." But as soon as we wish to be still more accurate, again we find ourselves sliding into more technical terms that specify shape in a geometric or mathematical way.

Size

A third group of common words of ordinary language that have mathematical meaning are those having to do with size, or quantity, before there is a definite, specific recognition of number or measurement. These words are in the list that follows.

big, great, large
little, small
size
long, high, tall, deep, far, thick, fat, full, wide
short, low, shallow, near, thin, empty, narrow
length, height, depth, distance, width, thickness

Here we may see (as we can see in many other places
also) some of the curious features of the classification of
ideas expressed in ordinary language. "High" and "tall"
both mean "long, in the direction up"; "deep" means "long,
in the direction down"; "far" means "long, in the direction
away." But there are also inconsistencies in the way these
words are used. In English we say "He is a tall man," not
"He is a high man"; "It is a high hill," not "It is a tall hill";
and we can say both "It is a high tree" and "It is a tall tree."
The idioms of ordinary language provide some fine traps to
fall into; mathematics, with its measurement of distance and
a statement of the direction of measurement, avoids many of
these traps.

Comparison

Another of the early stages in development of numerical ideas in man's conceptions of the world is grammatical
comparison of adjectives, as in "interesting, more interesting, most interesting." Here are some common everyday
words expressing mathematical ideas related to comparison.

-er (as in "taller")
-est (as in "tallest")
more
most
less
least
equal, as much as, as little as
unequal, not so much as

enough
good, better, best

For degrees of comparison, the earliest linguistic device is the use of different words for different degrees. Primitive men supposedly did not see the common feature being compared and so they made use of different word roots. Traces survive in a few instances in English, such as "good, better, best" using two different roots. In Latin, for this purpose, there are three words *bonus, melior, optimus,* showing three different roots — and providing an additional complication for the learner of language to remember by dint of memorizing. All three of these Latin roots appear in English words, for example, "bonus," "ameliorate," "optimist."

A less primitive type of linguistic device is the use of constant suffixes for comparison. In English these endings are "-er" and "-est." But the rules of English prevent us from using these endings for all adjectives because of pronunciation troubles; "interesting-er" and "interesting-est" would be unpleasant to our ears.

The most recent and the most general linguistic device is the use of the separate words "more" and "most." This device is the most efficient and the most precise. Furthermore, we can in this way take the concept which is implicit in the ending "-er" and say it by itself explicitly in a whole word, "more." Having expressed it in isolation, we are able to utter it or not utter it as we choose. Also, the device of the separate word has brought along the added advantage of combinations with "less" and "least," a kind of negative rather than positive comparison — very reasonable and doubtless missing from some languages.

In linguistic devices for comparison, we see clearly the characteristic evolution of an idea in language, the emerging or crystallizing out of the idea, the designation at last in separate words that we may use or not use at our choice. It is out of this process of evolution that mathematics has come.

Indefinite Numbers or Measurements

Another stage in the development of mathematical ideas in ordinary language is the recognition of indefinite numbers and measurements.

In most writing and talking it is objectionable to give numbers exactly. So the indefinite numbers are very useful. We can convey a meaning or give an explanation without having to be bothersomely precise. We say "He walked a little way into the room"; we don't say "He walked into the room 42 inches, plus or minus 4 inches." Following are the common words for indefinite numbers and measurements:

few
several, a handful of, a number of, a few
little
much, very
many, a lot of, a quantity of, a great deal of
some
"-s" for plural (as in "cats"), meaning "more than one"; also other endings or changes such as those appearing in "oxen" and "mice"
not very
fairly, rather, somewhat, partly
almost, nearly, very
entirely, altogether, quite

Definite Numbers

Almost as old as the indefinite numbers are the definite numbers. In fact, at one stage of development of language, the definite numbers were probably continued by the indefinite numbers: the ancient Tasmanian method of counting is reported to have been "one, two, many." Some of the words for the definite numbers are almost as old as any words to be found in the English language. In all those languages that have been studied enough to reveal the origin of the word "five," the word for "five" is derived from the word for "hand." The reason, of course, is the universal human habit of counting on fingers. Likewise in English the "t" in "ten" which is a contraction, is related to the "t" in "two" because of two hands denoting ten.

Here are some common everyday words dealing with the definite numbers.

one	no, none, naught, zero
two	once, twice
three, thir-	half, third, quarter
four	plus, and, -, (*i.e.*, "and" meaning
five, fif-	addition, as in "a hundred and
six	ten"; and the hyphen meaning
seven	addition as in "fifty-six")
eight	minus, less, but (as in "last but
nine	one")
ten, -teen, -ty	times, -s (as in "three fives" mean-
eleven	ing multiplication); also adja-
twelve, dozen	cency or juxtaposition, as when
twenty, score	two words are written next to
hundred	each other meaning multiplica-
thousand	tion as in "six hundred"
million	divided by, -th (as in "sixth"
billion	meaning "one divided by six")

The number words "zero," "million," "billion," "plus," "minus" are comparatively recent. In fact, "zero" is less of a common everyday word than some number words, because usually "none" or "nothing" will replace it. The Latin words *plus* and *minus*, originally meaning respectively "more" and "less," were taken into English and they received specific meanings denoting adding and subtracting.

Zero was apparently recognized as a number by the Babylonians about 1800 B.C. but afterwards forgotten. Apparently it was not recognized again as a number until about

200 B.C. in India. The word "zero" comes through Arabic from a Hindu word meaning "empty"—certainly a logical association. At the present time, missionaries who translate the Bible for small linguistic communities find from time to time a community that has no native word for "zero" and so they introduce a word for it.

"Million" is an Old French word coming from Old Italian *millione*, which is an augmentative (a word increasing the force of) of *mille*. *Mille* is both Italian and Latin, meaning "thousand."

"Billion" is a French word from Latin *bis* meaning "twice" and the word fragment "-illion" taken out of "million." Subsequently, "-illion" became a suffix for coining more large numbers. But words such as "trillion" and "quadrillion" are essentially technical words, and not to be considered part of the common everyday fund of knowledge of mathematical ideas.

Looking over this list of a few dozen ideas used for expressing numbers, we observe that with this small quantity of numbers and their combinations, we can express exactly far more than a billion billion numbers. This is a good example of the powers of language for expressing ideas by organizing them in combinations. This power mathematics shares with language, and greatly extends.

Order or Arrangement

The next group of common everyday words that express mathematical ideas are those which express order or arrangement:

> first, second, third, fourth, fifth, . . .
> next, last
> -th (as in "sixth," meaning sixth in order)
> arrange
> pattern, map, diagram
> collection, group; together

scatter, scattered, separated, spaced
one after another
in order, in sequence
one by one, two by two
even
uneven

The arrangements of collections of things constitute an interesting and important mathematical subject called "combinatorial analysis."

Variation or Approximation

The last group of common everyday words that deal with mathematical ideas are those having to do with changing, varying, and approximating:

by and large
on the average
about
roughly
approximately
range over
depend on
vary with
various

These words hint at two important branches of mathematics. One is called "statistics" and is the study of "about" in the sense of "approximately." The other is the study of "functions," which is the study of "it depends." Some mathematicians will tell you that most of mathematics consists of the study of the way one quantity may depend on another or vary as it varies.

Where Mathematics Came From: Ordinary Language

From these lists of common ordinary words that foreshadow useful and important mathematical ideas, we see clearly that:

Mathematics has emerged out of ordinary language and is itself a language. In fact, many of the properties of ordinary language appear in mathematics, and many properties that we ordinarily think of as mathematical appear also in ordinary language.

The Ability to Calculate

For example, take the property "calculation." This is a property characteristic of mathematics, by means of which we can reason forward from some statements called premises to other statements called conclusions, both using symbols that pay almost no attention to meaning. Yet, remarkably, we come out with true conclusions if the premises are true. This property is often present in ordinary language, as we can show with this piece of argument from a thoughtful and interesting book, *Language and Communication* by George A. Miller:

> Suppose we learn on good authority that all mantelops are lespeads, and that all lespeads hile. We can conclude immediately that all mantelops hile, and that any grimpet that does not hile is certainly not a mantelop. There may be of course lespeads that aren't mantelops; so hiling is not a sure sign of mantelopicity.

And, to paraphrase the next remark that Miller makes in his book, the fact that we have no idea what we are talking about does not prevent us from reasoning forward from one statement to another, and reasoning correctly besides. Yet all of this calculation is in ordinary language.

From Concrete to Abstract

We have all had much experience with the foregoing common words; we use them again and again. We put them into the processes of language and make other ideas out of them. One of the particularly important processes that we perform with them is to make abstract nouns out of them, nouns expressing a quality, property, or state.

For example, "in" gives rise to "inclusion," basically the quality of being in. "Over" gives rise to "superposition," essentially the quality of being placed over. "Size" or "bigness" is the quality of being big. "Distance" is the quality of being far, etc. If people could say "in-ness," "over-ness," "far-ness," the way we can say "bigness," we might be better off. The linguistic ending "-ness" expressing the idea "the quality of being . . ." corresponds to a precise operation in mathematics and logic covered in the branch of knowledge called "symbolic logic."

After an abstract noun such as "inclusion" is formed, the meaning spreads a little from its original meaning, and gradually the word takes on other meanings. Thus, "inclusion" means not only "being in" but also "being inside certain limits" and also "a thing which is inside certain limits," etc.

One of the important ways in which an abstract noun spreads is that it adds on the meaning of "degrees of" the quality. Thus "size" ("bigness") also has the meaning "degrees of bigness."

Groups of Mathematical Ideas

Mathematical ideas, expressed first in common everyday words (see the preceding lists) and second as abstract nouns, produce a group of common and useful expressions of mathematical ideas or concepts.

What are these concepts? Here is a list of them:

1) place, location, region, direction, space, position
2) shape, form, structure, organization
3) size, magnitude, extent, dimensions, distance
4) comparison, degree
5) indefinite number
6) definite number, quantity, amount, figure, measurement, scale
7) order, unit, count, arrangement, combination, operation, pattern
8) variation, range, average, deviations, approximation

These properties are, of course, among the commonest properties and relations of all things. These properties are studied in mathematics. What is the next step to understanding their mathematical treatment? The beginning of an answer to this question is given in the next chapter.

Understanding Mathematics

SUPPOSE THEN that it makes sense for you, who are reading this book, to be interested in mathematics.

How then shall we arrange for you to understand mathematics and arrange for you to acquire some of the tools of mathematics, so that you can solve some interesting and important mathematical problems?

The Organization of Knowledge: Ideas and Relations

The first step, I think, is to realize that all sensible branches of knowledge (including mathematics) are organized in essentially the same simple way: in terms of reasonable *ideas*, and sensible *relations* between them. So, if we learn the ideas and learn the relations between them, then we are a long way down the road of understanding that branch of knowledge.

Take, for example, the game of chess. The statements about chess in a book for beginners may start like this:

"Chess is a game for two players, who are called *White* and *Black*. The game is played on a square *board* of 64 squares, alternating white and black. When the players start the game, each has a set of 16 pieces, White having the white pieces and Black having the black pieces. The pieces are of six kinds called *king, queen, rook, bishop, knight,* and *pawn,* and have various powers, which will now be explained. . . ."

Let us take a close look at what these four sentences of explanation have told us:

1) We now know what kind of thing chess is: it is a game.
2) We now know how many players it requires: exactly two.
3) We have started to find out the materials needed to play the game; a board and 32 pieces of two colors, and six kinds.
4) In fact, we have already begun to acquire a little knowledge about nine special terms of chess (the italicized words above).

Mathematics, and every other sensible branch of knowledge, is like this simple example; it states certain ideas and certain relations. Such a subject can be understood in terms of certain reasonable ideas and certain sensible relations between them. Only subjects which are nonsense, like astrology, fortunetelling, superstitions, etc., are not organized in this way; and the so-called understanding that a person possesses of a nonsense subject is likely to vary from person to person according to those ideas and statements which each individual chooses to accept and believe.

The Size of a Branch of Knowledge

It follows from this argument that a branch of knowledge, a subject, has a *size*. The size is measured by the number of special terms which that subject deals with.

Chess is rather a small subject, because the total number of special terms is only about 30 or 35. Accordingly, the rules of playing chess can often be understood in about half an hour, and learned in about an hour and a half. Of course, for a person to become a good chess player takes many years of study and practice and some innate ability. But to play the game well enough to enjoy it takes only four or five hours of introduction—if one is really interested.

Mathematics is rather a big subject. The part of mathematics that is called *elementary*, studied in school and college by young people who are taking mathematics courses but are not specializing in mathematics, contains about 600 special terms.

Elementary mathematics has a number of branches, such as arithmetic, algebra, geometry, calculus, etc., and each of these has a number of subdivisions. And for any one of these branches or subdivisions, there is usually a fairly short list of special terms to be learned, and a fairly small collection of true statements about them, also to be learned. This amount of learning is not very great, and does not take excessively long—if one is really interested.

How to Understand a New Branch of Knowledge

The problem of learning a new subject, therefore, breaks down into the following steps:

- 1. IDEAS.   Identify the ideas which are special to the subject—find out the meaning of the special terms in the vocabulary of the subject.

How?

Well, one good way is to get hold of an introductory book on the subject that seems to explain well, and make notes of the words in the first few chapters which are evidently being used with special meanings. The evidence is sometimes that the words are carefully defined by the author, or they may be underlined or italicized, or they may occur in clarifying statements the author is making. For example, he may say something like "By . . . I mean . . . and not . . . ."

The easiest way, of course, is when the author is friendly

and frank with the reader and says at the start, "The special terms which I shall need to use are . . . and I explain them on pages . . ."

- 2. PROPERTIES AND RELATIONS. Find out the properties and relations of these ideas.

How?

By asking specific questions and hunting for the answers.

What sort of questions?

Examples are: What is the name of . . .? What are other names for . . .? What is the definition of . . .? and so on. These questions ask for statements of common properties and relations of ideas.

It is possible to collect about 35 of the "commonest properties and relations" of almost anything (see list on page 50 "Commonest Properties and Relations").

In studying the relations of an idea to other ideas, this list is often useful for suggesting questions and points that need to be considered. With this list as a guide (and some perseverance), one is able to get to the bottom of a great deal of knowledge.

Topic 3 in the list is "examples, instances" and is crucially important.

- 3. EXAMPLES. Next, find out examples, instances, illustrations, samples of the ideas and their properties and relations.

For example, it may be hard for anybody to define "number," but it is easy to give examples of numbers, like 2 or 3 or 7. And it may be hard to define "2," but it is very easy to give examples of classes or collections that have just two

Commonest Properties and Relations

1) Name, identification
2) Other names, repetition, equivalents, synonyms
3) Examples, instances
4) Essence, theme, nature, kernel
5) Definition, meaning, significance
6) Kind, sort, genus, species, class
7) Properties, nature, habits
8) Similar things, related things
9) Opposites, contrasts
10) Distinguishing characteristics, identifying properties
11) Things included in it, parts
12) Things of which it is a part
13) Context, environment, situation, field
14) Composition, material, substance
15) Structure, organization, construction
16) Activity, behavior, verb
17) Agents, doers, subject of verb
18) Products, object of verb
19) Manner, ways, adverbs
20) Size, dimensions, measurements
21) Quantity, number
22) Variation, range, average, deviations
23) Shape; form; solid, liquid or gas
24) Weight, density
25) Appearance, look, color, luster
26) Sound, smell, taste, feel
27) Place, location, position, extent, prevalence
28) Time, duration, age, persistency
29) History, origin, causes, development
30) Future, results, effects, predictions
31) Purpose, function, use, worth, value
32) Advantages
33) Disadvantages
34) Owners, users
35) Importance, relation to human affairs

members, like the two eyes of a human being, or the two wings of a bird.

And, in fact, if you cannot find an example of a certain idea after some diligent trying, perhaps the idea is not very important, and not worth too much attention or study after all.

- 4. MEMORIZING. Commit to memory at least some of the most essential ideas so that you can recall them when you want to.

In this area, a computing machine has a great advantage over any human being. Just feeding information into a computer will cause it to remember the information indefinitely, without any forgetting. But a human being usually has to exert a lot of mental effort in order to remember.

- 5. PROBLEM-SOLVING. Finally, practice answering questions, solving problems, in the territory so that you become familiar with how to apply the new ideas.

In fact, there is no advantage in learning a lot of new ideas without learning how to apply them, how to use them in situations. The finest definition of mathematical probability is not worth much unless one learns also how to calculate how often in the long run two dice when rolled will come up with double six (on the average, once in 36 throws).

None of the actions outlined above is beyond the powers of any person — if he is interested, and can bring himself to listen and to exert effort.

Example: Understanding Zero

Let us take for an example, the process of understanding the number zero.

Here are some true statements about zero. Following

each statement is a note showing which of the commonest properties and relations in the list on page 50 applies.

1) Zero is a number. [6. SPECIES]

2) It is the number that counts none or nothing. [5. DEFINITION]

3) It is marked 0 in our usual numeral writing. [2. SYNONYM]

4) The ancient Romans, however, had no numeral for it. Apparently they did not think of zero as a number. [29. HISTORY — A REMARK]

5) 0 is what you get when you take 13 away from 13, or when you subtract any number from itself. [7. A PROPERTY]

6) If you add 0 to 37, you get 37; and if you add 0 to any number, you get that number unchanged. [7. ANOTHER PROPERTY]

7) If you subtract 0 from 26, you get 26; and if you subtract 0 from any number, you get that number unchanged. [7. ANOTHER PROPERTY]

8) If you multiply 0 by 42, you get 0; and if you multiply together 0 and any number, you get 0. [7. ANOTHER PROPERTY]

9) Usually you are not allowed to divide by 0 — that is against the rules of arithmetic. [7. ANOTHER PROPERTY]

10) But if you do, and if you divide a number (that is not zero) by 0, as for example, dividing 15 by 0, the result is called infinity and is marked ∞, a sign that is like an 8 on its side.* [7. ANOTHER PROPERTY]

These are not all the properties and relations of zero; it is in fact one of the most remarkable and important of numbers. But if you know these statements about zero and have had some practice in applying them, you have a rather good understanding of zero.

* See Note on Infinity at the end of this chapter.

The Anchoring of New Knowledge upon Old Knowledge

Notice how even these ten rather simple statements about the properties of zero rely upon earlier knowledge. The meaning of these statements hinges upon the meaning of seven other terms of mathematics: "number, count, numeral, add, subtract, multiply, divide."

New knowledge is always anchored on old knowledge. The understanding of terms newly introduced relies upon, hinges upon, our understanding of old terms, terms previously introduced.

We might fear that this process would go back indefinitely, as in Augustus de Morgan's famous doggerel verse:

Great fleas have little fleas, upon their backs to bite 'em.
And little fleas have lesser fleas, and so ad infinitum.

But this does not happen; instead, there is a starting point.

This starting point is the knowledge that we have already acquired from our experiences when we reach the age of reflection, which may be age 13 or 14 for some young people and may be age 20 or 22 for others. Everybody who reaches the minimum cultural level in our society necessarily acquires an understanding of the meaning of some of the terms of mathematics, such as "count," "numeral," "add," "subtract." And the meaning of "multiply" and "divide" can be made clear in terms of "add," "subtract," and a few more fairly simple ideas.

When we reach the age of reflection, the age of thinking, we know already the meaning of some 50 to one hundred ideas of mathematics. In addition, we have had experiences which tell us the meaning of at least another 50 or one hundred ideas of mathematics, even if we have no knowledge of the technical names of the ideas. For example, anybody who has handled a lemon, and noticed that it is rather like a sphere but pulled out a little at the two ends, knows what a prolate spheroid is. And after that experience he does not need to feel disturbed over the term "prolate spheroid."

Our common everyday experience and its vocabulary is the starting point for acquiring a knowledge of mathematics.

Acquiring Power to Use Mathematical Tools

So much for the principles for understanding mathematics.

When it comes to acquiring power to use mathematical tools, study and practice are needed. For instance, a person can do a multiplication only if he has previously learned the procedure of multiplying and practiced dozens of examples.

Here, more is needed than just reading a book and passively absorbing the ideas in its pages. Action is needed. Repetition is needed. The situation here is like the situation in learning to swim: after a certain amount of explanation, more is needed than just reading a book. For swimming, you need a place to swim which has water that comes up at least to your shoulders, and then you actually get wet in the water and practice. So, for making mathematical tools your own, you will need to take out pencil and paper, and wrestle through examples and problems.

But this cold water advice does not have to be applied yet, right at this point.

Note on Infinity

Earlier we made some statements about the mathematical concept called infinity. We said:

"Usually you are not allowed to divide by zero — that is against the rules of arithmetic. But if you do, and if you divide a number (that is not zero) by zero, as for example, dividing 15 by zero, the result is called infinity, and is marked ∞, a sign that is like an 8 on its side."

These remarks about infinity can be made more precise at the cost of more words and more thought, as follows:

If you divide 15 by a number N which becomes smaller and smaller and smaller (without becoming zero), the result R (15 divided by N) becomes larger and larger and larger.

For example,

15 divided by one millionth = 15 million;

15 divided by one billionth = 15 billion;

15 divided by one trillionth = 15 trillion; and so on.

Now if N becomes zero, what does R become?

It is convenient to say that:

The result of 15 divided by N as N approaches zero becomes indefinitely large, and the limit is infinity.

And it is convenient to write:

$$\lim_{N \to 0} 15/N = \infty$$

Are there examples of infinity in the ordinary everyday world? Yes. Anyone who uses a camera with a changeable focus has had experience with infinity. In all such cameras, the distance of the lens from the film must be greater if the object being photographed is nearer, and less if the object is farther away. There is however a *shortest* distance of the lens from the film; and this distance corresponds to the *farthest* objects; it is a setting for "infinity." For a mountain ten miles away, or for the moon 240,000 miles away, the same shortest distance, the setting for infinity is used.

The Ideas of Mathematics

4

The Relative Importance of Ideas - Thousand-Horsepower Ideas -
Flypower Ideas - The Most Important Ideas of Mathematics - The
Paths to Understanding Important Mathematical Ideas

WE HAVE NOW TOUCHED on two of the ideas of mathematics. One of these ideas is *zero*; and we have put down
over a dozen statements about zero. The second idea we
have touched on is the idea of *infinity*, and so far we have
made only a few statements about it. One of these statements, for example, was that infinity is symbolized ∞, like a
figure 8 on its side.

Now of course there are a great many more ideas in
mathematics. But since we have limited time and energy,
we need to sort the ideas of mathematics according to their
importance.

The Relative Importance of Ideas

In any field, some ideas are important and some are
trivial. The importance of an idea is measured by
- the number of things to which the idea applies—its
  applicability;
- how often the idea is used in discussion and explanation—its relative frequency;
- to what extent other ideas flow from it or can be derived from it—its fruitfulness;
- to what extent the idea benefits human beings—its
  practical advantages; and similar factors.

In the field of biology for example, the theory of evolution is a profoundly important idea. It is much more important than, for example, the classification of bears by the color

56

of their fur: black, brown, white, or grizzly. It is true that more people know about the colors of bears than understand the theory of evolution. But the theory of evolution applies to all living species of all colors; it is far more widely applicable. Also, it is immensely fruitful in the conclusions that can be drawn about living species. Furthermore, evolution can be put to use for human beings in controlled situations involving plant breeding and animal husbandry. In the field of mathematics the same general considerations about the importance of ideas are valid and can be applied.

Thousand-Horsepower Ideas

Some of the ideas of mathematics are very powerful, as powerful figuratively as a thousand-horsepower engine. These ideas occur often and apply widely in human affairs. They give answers to many problems. They provide ways for understanding situations and processes. They give pictures, diagrams, ways of thinking, models that you can carry around in your mind and that help to explain events and processes happening in the world.

What are some examples of these ideas? One example is the idea of "next along a line." If you are riding on a railroad to go to Mystic, a question that you might well ask the conductor is "What is the last stop before Mystic?" After he tells you "Westerly," you can, when the train is at Westerly, start putting your luggage together so as to get off at the next station. This is because you can think of stations on a railroad as successive marks along a line, or as successive beads along a string, etc. Your mental picture is that of a series of separate entities coming one after another in a sequence. This idea of a sequence or a series is a common mathematical idea of great power and widespread usefulness.

Another example of a mathematical idea of great power is the process for multiplying together two numbers in ordinary decimal notation (Arabic numerals). The process works for all numbers; it works for all cases of multiplication; it is easy, direct, quick, and widely useful. Yet as a process in common use by human beings, it has existed only since the sixteenth century. The previous process, multiplying numbers using Roman numerals, required far more mental effort.

Flypower Ideas

But not all of the ideas of mathematics are thousand-horsepower ideas: some are essentially frills and trifles. And so far as we can see, they will always remain only frills and trifles. Their efficacy is a few flypower. These ideas apply only narrowly. They give answers to only a few problems. They are models or ways of thinking for only a very few situations. They do not give many clues to the behavior of the real world.

An example of a flypower idea is this: if you take the number 142,857 and add it to itself, you will get the same digits in the same order but starting at a different digit: 285,714. This is an example of what is called *cyclic* order. Now if you add 142,857 to 285,714, again you get the same digits in the same order, but starting at a different digit: 428,571. This preservation of cyclic order when one number is added to another is remarkable, amusing, puzzling, and it leads to interesting questions; it has, in fact, led to the investigation of the behavior of similar numbers (for example 153,846 plus 461,538 equals 615,384), nearly all of them very large numbers. But when all is said and done, the idea of cyclic order of digits preserved when numbers are added does not apply widely, does not give answers to many problems, and does not give power to understand many parts of the world. It is a flypower idea.

Another more pervasive and rather misleading flypower idea is implied by many mathematical illustrations and exercises actually found in textbooks and the teaching of mathematics. This is the idea that answers to problems will come out neatly, elegantly, with easy arithmetic, and an aesthetic effect.

For example, in learning arithmetic you may come across a problem of finding the amount of wallpaper needed to paper a room. Commonly, the problem as given to you in a textbook will describe the room with easy dimensions, such as 20 feet long, 15 feet wide, and 9 feet high. But if you actually have to put wallpaper on a real room in the real world, you are likely to find that the room may be 18 feet 4 inches long, 14 feet 2 inches wide, and 9 feet 3 inches high; it will have windows and doors that cannot be papered, and wainscoting or molding that should not be papered; the design in the wallpaper has to be observed and conformed with, as the different strips of wallpaper are placed; the amount of overlap of the strips has to be known; etc.; and you will not wind up with a neat, elegant, and aesthetic answer.

Neat and elegant answers are almost missing in the real world. In truth, you and I should learn arithmetic with a desk calculator at our elbow, so that we can delegate to the machine the annoying routine labor of multiplying out such a calculation as 18.33 feet times 14.17 feet. If we do not have the calculator, we need to learn how to make approximate calculations so that we do no more work and spend no more time than necessary.

The Most Important Ideas of Mathematics

What are the most important ideas of mathematics upon which we should concentrate our attention?

If you could persuade each of a hundred mathematicians to give you a list of the 15 or 20 ideas in mathematics which he considered the most important, you would probably get at least 90 different lists. You might even get a hundred different lists! (Of course, many of the hundred mathematicians might be very unwilling to accept the viewpoint that there are 15 or 20 mathematical ideas which have maximum im-

portance and interest.) But even so, there would be a good
many ideas in common on those lists, for it is undeniable that
the most important ideas of mathematics have obvious and
outstanding importance.

The important ideas of mathematics that we shall try to
explain in this guide are these:

- The rough and approximate numbers, and the
  numerical ideas associated with them
  [THE NUMBERS THAT ARE USED OFTEN]
- The powerful (yet simple) techniques for rapid
  estimating, which are usually not taught in or-
  dinary arithmetic
  [THE ARITHMETIC OF ESTIMATING]
- Using symbols for designating unknown or varying
  quantities and expressing relations between them
  [VARIABLES AND FORMULAS]
- Using graphs and tables to express the corresponding changes of related quantities
  [FUNCTIONS AND GRAPHS]
- The two basic ideas of the calculus: instantaneous
  rate of change, and the limit of a sum of a larger
  and larger number of smaller and smaller bits
  [DERIVATIVES AND INTEGRALS]
- Some basic ideas of algebra: what to do when you
  have some expression equal to some other expres-
  sion, and you want to solve for numbers which
  make the equation true   [EQUATIONS]
- The unavoidable extensions of the idea of number
  to include the idea of angles and directions
  [ANGLES]
- Two basic ideas of logic: properties and relations
  [PROPERTIES AND RELATIONS]
- The nature of probability, and chances
  [PROBABILITY AND FREQUENCY DISTRIBUTIONS]

It is sad to have to say that many very important and interesting ideas of mathematics are not in this list, and have to be left out of this book. So this book needs to be essentially an introduction; after you have read and digested the discussion of the important mathematical ideas in this book, then turn to other books, and read and investigate further.

The Paths to Understanding Important Mathematical Ideas

In any field of knowledge such as mathematics, some persons who are reputed to be the recognized experts insist that you as a learner must approach the heights of knowledge in that field by using the traditional long path. They assert that you need to learn the unimportant ideas along the way as well as the important ones, and that you need to learn them in an approved sequence, until finally you reach the pinnacles by the approved path. These people say that you have to take courses, accumulate credits, get degrees, spend time, and go over the established hurdles in the approved way. These people say, "You will recognize a man educated in mathematics by his background: the record of his education and experience, the record of the courses for which he has received credit, the time he has spent learning."

Then there are other people who say that there may be many paths, even short and steep ones, to the heights of knowledge in that field. They believe that you as a learner *may* be able to travel a steep path quickly. These people say, "You will recognize a man educated in mathematics by what he can do, by his behavior: the questions he can answer, the problems he can solve, the mathematical situations he can deal with sensibly."

As you may easily guess, I belong to this second group. I do not care how many calculus courses a man has taken — but if he can come into my office, tell me in answer to a question what an integral is, give me a good example, and then find an integral in a simple situation that I select and sketch out in front of him, then I think he has learned some mathematics, and I have respect and admiration for him.

If you have reached the age of reflection, if you are eager to understand some of the most important and interesting mathematical ideas that there are, and if you are satisfied to verify your understanding by what you can do with actual questions and problems—then I hope and believe this guide will be of help to you.

Part Two

ROUGHLY AND APPROXIMATELY

The Numbers That Are Used Often

OUR ORDINARY EVERYDAY WORLD is full of rough and approximate numbers, numerical inexactness. This is very reasonable. A toastmaster at a dinner invites the guest of honor to "say a few words." He does not invite the guest to "say 1294 words to our audience of 73 this evening." A book on political geography opened at random says, "The history of the next three centuries is the history of the struggle for supremacy of these northwest European countries." The sentence does not begin: "The history of the next 314 years, 11 months and 19 days is the history of . . ." A newspaper refers on page 1 to a man "who was pardoned last Friday, after having served 22 months of a ten-year sentence on charges of espionage." If you or I, instead of a reporter, were telling this, we would probably say "almost two years" instead of "22 months"; that is the way people actually talk about numbers in ordinary everyday situations.

5

The Numbers That Occur in the Common Everyday World

Ordinary talking, listening, and thinking are so filled with certain common, familiar, widely accepted numerical ideas that we hardly ever stop to notice them. Although they are unobtrusive, they are valuable tools of language and of mathematics. To confirm this statement, let us look back over the previous paragraph and notice some of the contrasts between the common everyday numerical ideas and the more technical numerical ideas there expressed. The more technical numerical ideas are: 1294, 73, 314, 11, 19, 22; the more common numerical ideas are "a few" in "a few words," "three" in "three centuries," "one" in "page one," "ten" in "ten-year," and "almost two."

In the phrase "say a few words," the use of "a few" does not distract the attention of the audience as would happen if the toastmaster should say "1294 words"; it accords with the principle in speaking that one should be economical in stirring up ideas in the listener's mind. The number "three" in "three centuries" is another example. Here "three" does not imply "exactly three" but only "approximately three," in the sense that the period of time referred to may be anywhere from about two and a half centuries to about three and a half centuries. The number "one" in "page 1" is a third example but an example of rather a different kind. Here "one" in "page 1" is of course accurate; we do not mean "perhaps page 1 or page 2 or page 3," and a newspaper cannot have a page $1\frac{1}{2}$; but the number one is so common and so accepted in ordinary conversation that although it is accurate, it is not felt to be technical and distracting.

Only a Few Numbers Are Used Often

Now it is an interesting fact, which many people have not noticed, that in the common everyday world only a few numbers are used often—in fact fewer than 60. In other words, in ordinary nontechnical human affairs, some numbers occur very frequently; some other numbers occur from time to time; and most numbers hardly ever occur.

This fact is quite the opposite of the usual impression about numbers that we receive when learning arithmetic.

When you and I learned arithmetic in grade school, we found out about a large collection of numbers which could be made by putting together many of the *digits* 0, 1, 2, 3, 4, 5, 6, 7, 8, 9, in any way that the teacher chose. For example, I was given exercises in subtracting, such as:

$$
\begin{array}{r} 34158 \\ -\ 9641 \\ \hline \end{array}
\qquad
\begin{array}{r} 143452 \\ -\ 79353 \\ \hline \end{array}
\qquad
\begin{array}{r} 89086 \\ -11597 \\ \hline \end{array}
$$

or in adding, such as:

$$
\begin{array}{r}
257963 \\
+\ 148327 \\
+9651846 \\
+\ 770392 \\
+2451628 \\
\hline
\end{array}
$$

or in multiplying, such as:

$$
\begin{array}{r}
94685 \\
\times 83567 \\
\hline
\end{array}
$$

In exercises like these a teacher tries to make sure that the same numbers are not repeated. Such exercises are probably a good way for learning the processes of arithmetic; but they do not draw our attention to the situation in the common everyday world, where the same simple numbers are used over and over.

The Familiar Numbers

What are the familiar numbers and numerical ideas of the common everyday world? These are the ideas which we can use in our ordinary conversation without our listeners' thinking that we are being technical.

A reasonable way of selecting them is to rely on our habits and experience in using English to guide us in deciding whether or not a numerical idea we think of expressing is likely to be thoroughly familiar. We have lots of such experience, for nearly always, when we talk, we want to be understood, and we try to choose words so that our listeners may understand us easily and not be surprised, distracted, or shocked. We try not to say "Extinguish the illumination" — instead we say "Turn out the light."

If we use this commonsense guide, we can say that the familiar numbers of the ordinary everyday context are all simple combinations of, at most, two terms selected out of the collection of very fundamental English terms that may be used to express numbers. For as soon as a speaker selects three or more terms out of this collection, his listeners begin to think he is getting technical.

The first kind of term used to express the familiar numbers consists of the common numerical words that count units. There are 14 such words expressing 12 numerical ideas: one, a, two, three, four, five, six, seven, eight, nine, ten, eleven, twelve, dozen.

The second kind of term used to express familiar numbers consists of the common words for 10, 100, 1000, and 1,000,000. There are five terms (two suffixes, three words) expressing four numerical ideas: "-teen," "-ty" (for "ten" as in "fourteen" and "seventy"); "hundred, thousand, million." We probably should leave out "billion," because most people have to stop to think how big a billion is: in the United States, a digit one with nine zero digits written after it — a thousand million; in Great Britain, a digit one with 12 zero digits written after it — a million million.

Third, there is a miscellaneous group of 12 definite numerical terms: "first, second, third, half, quarter"; "-th" as in "tenth"; "zero, naught, no," and their partial equivalents "none, nothing, nobody." Only three numerical ideas are here expressed. Examples are: "tenth" meaning number 10 in sequence; "fifth" meaning "one divided by five" as in "a fifth," one of five equal parts; and the idea of zero. The 12 words for three ideas are characteristic of the irregular way in which natural language has grown.

Fourth, there are nine terms (and perhaps more) expressing the indefinite numbers. These are often used in such a way that the listener is given added information: how approximate the number is, what range or leeway roughly applies:

few	many	every
little	much	all
some	most	several

Finally, there are some modifiers. The terms "more than," "less than," "about," "almost," "nearly," "at least," etc., give more information about range or leeway. In addition we have: "or" as in "six or eight"; "and" as in "a hundred and ten"; and the commonest of all the numerical ideas in English, the ending "-s" designating plural or "more than one" (and some equivalent endings like "-en" in "oxen").

This gives a total count of about 50 terms. These terms may be combined in a great number of ways that take advantage of the combining powers of English. But only some of the combinations express familiar numerical ideas, depending basically on the number of terms used in a combination; for example, "tenth" uses two terms, "ten" and "-th."

Ordinarily it seems that if you choose not more than two terms (and perhaps one or two modifiers) you have a familiar numerical idea, and you can use it anywhere without fearing that your listeners may be distracted:

sixty: two terms, "six," "-ty";
half million: two terms, "half," "million."

But if you choose as many as five terms, you do not get a familiar number belonging to the ordinary everyday context, but instead a technical number belonging to the context of arithmetic:

"four hundred eighty-seven."

How Many Familiar Numbers Are There?

How many familiar numbers are there altogether? To make a rough estimate, we can combine the dozen numbers 1 to 12 with the numbers based on ten represented by millionth, thousandth, hundredth, tenth, units, tens, hundreds, thousands, millions, and we come out with 12 times 9 or about a hundred. If we now include the indefinite numbers, we perhaps increase the total up to some figure near 150. This surprisingly small total of different familiar numerical ideas is sufficient for our common everyday world. Yet the words (and other terms) that express them occupy more than 5 percent of all spoken English language; by far the most frequent of them are "-s," the designation of plural, and "a" designating "one."

Framework for Making Decisions

The familiar numerical ideas provide a framework within which sizes, distances, and other magnitudes of the everyday world can be arranged. In some societies more primitive than our own, there are just four numbers that make up the total framework of numerical ideas in the society: "one," "two," "three," "many." We have a richer framework.

The thinking that we do and a great many of the choices and decisions that we make do not require precise numbers, but they do require approximate numbers. For example, when we are thinking about buying something, the problem of deciding often separates into three parts: if it costs less than one figure (a dollar, say), then we know we can buy it without hesitating; if it costs more than another figure (ten dollars, say), then we know we have to get along without buying it; and only if the price is in between these two bounds do we need to do more thinking about buying, and in such case find out the actual price, and weigh advantage against cost. (Of course, depending on the kind of article wanted, the two bounds may be very different from one dollar and ten dollars.)

The Numbers of One Significant Figure

Now the familiar numerical ideas we have been talking about are not always easy to deal with arithmetically. Their main virtue is that they show roughly about how big a number is, and roughly how much precision is intended. But we cannot calculate easily with all the familiar numerical ideas. For example, how much is a few plus a few? It depends. If you took much away from many, would you have a few left? It depends.

Besides, there are big gaps at the big end and the little end of the scale of the familiar numbers. With two terms taken from the list of familiar numbers, the largest definite number we can make is "million million." There is a very big gap between that and the next smaller number, "thousand million." Also, the smallest number we can make with two terms is "millionth"; the next smallest number producible is "thousandth."

We can agree that the familiar numbers have undesirable drawbacks, and that we need to make them systematic enough so that we can calculate well with them. This need leads us to what are called the "numbers of one significant figure." These numbers consist of one single digit 1, 2, 3, 4, 5, 6, 7, 8, or 9, with or without some zeros. For example, 3, 4, 70, 600, 3000, 20,000, and 60,000,000 are all numbers of one significant figure. So are 0.2 meaning two tenths; 0.005 meaning five thousandths; etc.

There is a standard process for going from more precise numbers to less precise numbers; it is called *rounding off*. The usual way to round off a more precise number is to replace it by the nearest one of the less precise numbers. For example, 62 as a more precise number becomes 60 as a less precise number, and 67 becomes 70. To round off 65, which is halfway between 60 and 70, the usual rule is to take it to the next higher less precise number, which in this case is 70. The number 66.8502 may be rounded off successively to 66.850, 66.85, 66.9, 67, 70, depending on how many "significant figures" we desire to keep.

It is easy to see that some of the familiar numerical terms are not numbers of one significant figure. Eleven is not, and is rounded off to ten; 15 is not, and is rounded off to 20. This points up the fact that sometimes, and particularly between 10 and 20, or between 100 and 200, etc., we may need to be more precise than the nearest number of one significant figure. To take care of the gap between 1 and 2, the Romans, in fact, had in Latin a familiar numerical idea that English does not have: *sesqui* meaning "one and a half." In English "sesqui" can only be used as a part of a word; a "sesquicentennial" is an anniversary 150 years after the event.

What about the process for going from a less precise number or even an indefinite number to a more precise number? There is no standard way for doing this; so we fall back on those three ancient human processes for making decisions: experience, imagination, and judgment. "A few words" in the case of the after-dinner speaker would be enough words to fill up perhaps five minutes of talking, and if a man can speak at about 200 words a minute, this would come to about a thousand words. "A few words" in the case of a telegram would mean less than 15, because 15 is the most one can send for the regular minimum cost.

Because of the nature of the rounding-off process, we know that once in a long while a less precise number stands for a more precise number exactly equal to it. Most of the time, however, the less precise number, or rounded-off number, may represent any one of a large group of numbers. For example: a distance of "about" four inches stands for any distance between $3\frac{1}{2}$ inches and $4\frac{1}{2}$ inches; the number 2200 represents any number from 2150 to 2249 inclusive; and the number 4000 represents any number from 3500 to 4499 inclusive. In many cases, the bigger the round number, the larger the group of numbers any one of which it may stand for; so 2,000,000 as a round number would stand for any number between $1\frac{1}{2}$ and $2\frac{1}{2}$ millions.

The Numbers That Occur in the Scientific World: Numbers in Scientific Normal Form

The numbers of one significant figure are common and important in the everyday world. But there is a parallel to them in the common and important numbers of the modern scientific world. These are numbers which have been expressed in what is called *scientific normal form*.

An example of a number in this form is 4.37×10^{20}: which means 4 and 37 hundredths times ten "to the twentieth *power*," 10 as a multiplier 20 times, or 1 followed by 20 zeros. The small raised number (in this case 20) denotes the "power" of ten.

This number in the language of school arithmetic is 437,000,000,000,000,000,000; or four hundred thirty-seven billion billion, if we try to say it in words. The closest of the familiar numerical ideas is perhaps "millions of millions." The closest number of one significant figure is 400,000,000,000,000,000,000 or 4×10^{20}.

A number in scientific normal form is made up of two parts multiplied together; the first part is written as an ordinary number between 1.000 . . . and 9.999 . . .; and the second part is written as 10^n, 10 with a small number (n) written in the upper right-hand corner that tells the *power* of ten—the number of 10's that have been multiplied together. For example, 10^2 is 10×10 or 100; 10^6 is $10 \times 10 \times 10 \times 10 \times 10 \times 10$ or 1,000,000, a million; 10^{-1} (ten to the minus one power) is $1/10$ or one tenth; 10^{-2} (ten to the minus two power) is $1/100$ or one hundredth; etc. The number n is called the *power* or *exponent* of ten; when written with a minus sign in front of it, it refers to a decimal fraction, as illustrated. The first part of the number in scientific normal form is called the *coefficient*; the second part of the number in scientific normal form is called the *power of ten*.

Numbers expressed in scientific normal form give us some great advantages in writing and working with very large and very small numbers used in present-day science. Thus a physicist may write down the mass of the earth as 5.9×10^{27} grams instead of writing 5,900,000,000,000,000,-000,000,000,000 grams.

Significant Figures

In addition, when the physicist writes 5.9, he also says that the true figure he refers to is somewhere between 5.85 and 5.94, or else he would have written one more digit. The 5 and 9 in the 5.9 are called two *significant figures*.

The significant figures, or more correctly the *significant digits*, of any number are the digits in the coefficient when it is written in scientific normal form. For example, in 12 million, or 1.2×10^6, the 1 and the 2 are the significant figures or digits. In .000376, or 3.76×10^{-4}, the 3, 7 and 6 are the significant digits. In 30,060,000 there are four significant digits, for it may be written 3.006×10^7. The number .0028 may be written 2.8×10^{-3}; so it contains two significant figures. If a man says "The number of pages is exactly 1000," then this is one of the rare cases when the zeros are significant, and this is a precise number containing four significant digits. In the absence of more precise information, however, we would consider the 1000 a round number containing only one significant digit.

The coefficient of a number written in scientific normal form contains the number's significant figures. But the other important part of the number is its power of ten. The power of ten reported in a number written in scientific normal form is called its *order of magnitude*; it reports concisely that number's essential "mathematical size."

How Many Numbers Are There in the Scientific World?

Previously we asked the question, How many familiar numbers are there in the common everyday world? and came out with the answer, Somewhere between a hundred and 200. Now let us ask this question:

PROBLEM: How many numbers in scientific normal form are there in the modern scientific world?

Solution:

1) The largest power of ten used in the scientific world is about 10^{120}. The smallest power of ten used is about 10^{-40}. The range from minus 40 to plus 120 is therefore 160.

2) The greatest accuracy with which any number can be observed by scientists ordinarily does not yield more than six or seven digits for the coefficient. So the numbers needed in the scientific world for coefficients would be the numbers from 1 to 9, 1.0 to 9.9, 1.00 to 9.99, etc., up to 1.000000 to 9.999999. They total $9 + 90 + 900 + 9000 + 90,000 + 900,000 + 9,000,000$, or about 10,000,000; which is 10^7.

3) Any of the 10^7 coefficients can be used with any of the 160 powers of ten.

4) Therefore, multiplying together, we obtain 160 times 10 million, or 1.6 billion—about $1\frac{1}{2}$ billion numbers—as the total quantity of numbers used in the scientific world.

So, for the rough and approximate purposes of scientists, and even the most accurate purposes that they can use their instruments for, they do not need many more than about two billion numbers.

All the Numbers That There Are

We have now totaled two sets of numbers, one the set of numbers used in the common everyday world, between a hundred and 200, and the other the set of numbers that are commonly used in the scientific world, about two billion. Both of these sets of numbers are *finite*, in the sense that there is an end to them.

But what is the number of all numbers?

This number is infinite, because the question is equivalent to asking, What is the largest number?

However, it is true that for almost all the important purposes of human beings, numbers are not an infinite collection — there *is* an end to them. We live in a rough and approximate, finite environment on earth, in space. And in this environment there are some things we can grasp entirely, including the set of all numbers for which we have a use.

Estimating and Its Simple Arithmetic

AS WE HAVE SHOWN in the preceding chapter, inaccurate, inexact, rough and approximate numbers — round numbers, numbers of one significant figure — fill the common everyday world. Why? Because these numbers, though rough and approximate, nevertheless give us a great deal of valuable information. They help us form an idea of the extent to which some quality or quantity is present. They allow us to make up our minds about many questions. They enable us to make decisions. These numbers are the results of estimating. Now, just what do we mean by estimating?

What Is Estimating?

Estimating, according to the dictionary, means forming an idea of quantities without actually counting or measuring; it means fixing roughly or approximately the size or the cost or the worth or the magnitude of something or other.

For example, suppose I inquire, "How far is it from New York to Boston?" And some friend answers me, "Oh, it takes about four hours on a fast train — if the train travels 50 miles an hour on the average, the distance would be about 200 miles." My friend certainly does not count or measure the miles; his figure is an estimate. (If, to verify, we look up the distance in an almanac, we find that the airline distance is given as 188 miles; if we look in a train timetable, the rail distance is given as 229 miles; and the motoring distance, on a current road map, is given as 209 miles. So the 200 miles is not a bad estimate.)

Why Is Estimating Important?

Estimating is an important process, for over and over again, the result of estimating is essential for answering questions and making decisions. For example, if my question is "Shall I walk?" often all I need to know about the distance is an estimate of whether it is more or less than a few blocks, and that often settles completely whether it is a good idea for me to walk or not.

If my question is "Shall I try to see both John Jones at Dynamics, Inc., and Samuel Smith at Applications Corporation on Thursday afternoon?" I think over the distances, the time required, and the possible ways of traveling, and as a result of estimating, decide whether or not it is sensible to try.

When telephoning Mr. Jones, I may find out from a secretary that he is not in, and then I say, "When will he come back?" because I need to decide how to reach him. A poor secretary handles this question as if it were ordinary arithmetic; she says "I don't know when he will come back." This answer leaves me still unable to decide. But a good secretary realizes that I am trying to estimate a time when I can reach Mr. Jones and talk to him; she says, "He did not say when he would come back, but I am sure that he will be back by four o'clock, and if you call a little after four, you should be able to reach him." She has a feeling for the difference between ordinary arithmetic and the arithmetic for estimating, and she helps me to make my decision.

How to Estimate

Estimating is regularly made up of two separate and distinct processes:

1) Gathering at least some information or data to base the estimate on: observations, facts, statistics, reasonable assumptions, etc.

2) Combining that information (using reasoning, arithmetic, etc.) so as to construct the estimate you are interested in.

Both these processes are shown in the example given earlier: "How far is it from New York to Boston?" Two observations are reported: "It takes about four hours on a fast train," and "A fast train is likely to travel about 50 miles an hour." There is one combination of these two pieces of information: ordinary arithmetical multiplication: $4 \times 50 = 200$. These two processes are regularly found in all kinds of estimating. In order to estimate well, of course, we need to find out how to perform these two processes efficiently.

Now let us look into the second process first, the process of reasoning about the data so as to obtain an estimate. A little later on we will look into the first process — choosing the data to start the estimate with.

The Arithmetic for Estimating

Although there are many branches of reasoning and mathematics for combining information, if we intend to be rough and approximate and come out with round-number answers to many questions — in other words if we intend to estimate — then most of the time we will be doing arithmetic. In estimating, arithmetic is central.

But the arithmetic that is suited to estimating is not ordinary arithmetic. It is easier and simpler than ordinary arithmetic. It consists of ordinary arithmetic stripped down and streamlined to be efficient for estimating. We shall designate this kind of arithmetic the *arithmetic for estimating*, or *estimating-arithmetic*. (We might even coin a blend word and call it *esti-matic!*)

The contrasts between ordinary arithmetic and the arithmetic for estimating are rather remarkable. Ordinary arithmetic nearly always comes out with rather precise numbers, usually numbers of three or more significant figures. The arithmetic for estimating comes out with round numbers, usually numbers of one significant figure.

Ordinary arithmetic often requires us to carry out what is for human beings a prodigious amount of work—so that ordinarily we must delegate the work to calculating machines or automatic computers in order to carry it out efficiently in the real world of business and society. But the arithmetic for estimating nearly always requires so little work that the back of an envelope is enough paper.

Ordinary arithmetic is what you use when you receive salary, put money in the bank, and pay bills. You have to be rather exact down to dollars and cents, or somebody feels cheated. For example, if you sought to draw $186 from the bank, the bank would not think of giving you the round sum of $200. You also use ordinary arithmetic when you are buying goods in a store and receiving change from a ten-dollar bill.

The arithmetic for estimating does not need to be nearly so exact as ordinary arithmetic. So let us see how ordinary arithmetic is modified so as to be efficient as the arithmetic for estimating.

ADDITION

The first process in ordinary arithmetic is addition. It is often rather a troublesome process. As soon as the numbers contain many digits, the mental work becomes almost intolerable, and very few human beings can do it easily, correctly, or willingly. In practice, people often use adding machines to add a sheet of figures; and the adding machine usually prints out each keyed-in number (as well as the total) on a paper tape, so that not only can you add correctly with the machine, but also you can tell at once, by comparing the tape and the original sheet, whether each number was inserted correctly. All banks, and many other businesses, use adding machines; and a clerk frequently attaches to a group of papers the printed tape showing the numbers added as proof that he added the numbers correctly.

But when we engage in estimating, addition becomes a great deal simpler. Let us take a sample problem.

PROBLEM 1:   On a trip to the supermarket you buy 20 items. You notice the prices as you pick the articles up and put them in your shopping cart. The prices are as follows:

.19	.63	.91	.77
.39	.73	.22	.96
1.15	.28	1.37	2.41
.36	.48	.89	.60
.78	1.54	.57	.31

About how much change should you receive out of a $20 bill?

Solution: First, by scanning through the list of numbers, we reach the conclusion that a typical average price for an item seems to be about 70 cents. Since there are 20 items, we would expect the total cost to be about 20 times 70 cents, or $14. So we would expect, as change out of a $20 bill, $20 less $14, or about $6. This is our first estimate, which is *Answer No. 1.*

Now let us make a second estimate a little more carefully. Let's round off each figure to the nearest multiple of ten cents:

2	6	9	8
4	7	2	10
12	3	14	24
4	5	9	6
8	15	6	3

and then add the results: the result is 157, meaning $15.70 total cost. So the change we would expect out of a $20 bill would be $4.30. This is our second estimate — *Answer No. 2.*

When we get to the check-out clerk, the cash register tape shows that the total cost is $15.54, and our change is $4.46. Our estimates were not bad.

PROBLEM 2: Estimate the sum of the numbers in Table 1, below.

TABLE 1

3,061,743	3,934,224	591,024	10,498,012
749,587	2,621,073	1,325,510	791,896
1,909,511	1,905,299	160,083	2,117,027
10,586,223	2,944,806	533,242	652,740
1,325,089	2,683,516	4,835,329	3,291,718
2,007,280	913,774	681,187	7,711,194
318,085	2,343,001	14,830,192	688,862
802,178	4,690,514	4,061,929	377,747
2,771,305	6,371,766	619,636	3,318,680
3,444,578	2,982,483	7,946,627	2,378,963
588,637	2,178,914	2,233,351	2,005,552
8,712,176	3,954,653	1,521,341	3,434,575
			290,529

Solution: First, we observe that we have 49 numbers (say, 50 numbers); and a typical average figure seems to be about 3 million. So we expect that as a very rough estimate we would have 50 times 3 million as the sum. So our first estimate is about 150 million—*Answer No. 1.*

Now, let us make a second estimate a little more carefully. Suppose we round off each figure to the nearest million, and then add the results (see facing page).

To save work, we can group them as four 0's, plus thirteen 1's, plus ten 2's, plus ten 3's, plus three 4's, plus two 5's, plus 6, 8, 8, 9, 10, 11, and 15; the result is equal to 152; since we are counting in millions, the estimated sum is 152 million. The 2 in the 152 is not reliable; so rounding this off we

3	4	1	10
1	3	1	1
2	2	0	2
11	3	1	1
1	3	5	3
2	1	1	8
0	2	15	1
1	5	4	0
3	6	1	3
3	3	8	2
1	2	2	2
9	4	2	3
			0

have 150 million. This, then, is our second estimate, 150 million—*Answer No. 2*.

Now it just happens that these figures were the reported populations in 1950 of 48 states of the United States and the District of Columbia; their accurate total is 150,697,361, or, rounded off, 151 million. So our estimates are not bad, and are in fact closer than we would ordinarily expect.

Actually, for the second estimate, it is not necessary to rewrite the figures. All we need to do is:

1) add the millions (the first two columns of figures) actually shown in the problem, starting with 3, 1, 10, and finishing up with 2, 2, 3—which gives a total of 124; then

2) pay attention to the third column of figures (the column reporting the hundred thousands) starting with 0, 7, 9, and finishing with 0, 4, 2, and count the cases where 5, 6, 7, 8, or 9 appear in this column— which gives 28; and finally add these two amounts, which gives 152, as before. The same result will be obtained, since the two processes are equivalent.

What conclusions can we draw from the two examples

of estimating sums? There are several. One good procedure for estimating a sum is:

- estimate the average item to be added, A;
- count the number of items to be added, N;
- then take A times N as an estimate of the sum.

When this procedure is used, addition turns into multiplication.

Another good procedure for estimating a sum is:

- add the most significant figures only, obtaining S;
- for the first column of figures ignored, count the cases where 5, 6, 7, 8, 9 (the higher half of the digits 0 to 9) occur, obtaining H;
- then S plus H is an estimate of the sum.

An important consequence of the rules for addition in estimating-arithmetic is that addition every now and then reduces simply to discovering which is the largest of a set of numbers. For example:

PROBLEM 3: Estimate the sum of 4000, 20 million, and 30. *Answer:* 20 million.

SUBTRACTION

Subtraction, in estimating-arithmetic, may be separated into several cases.

One case is where the number being subtracted is quite small, and the other number is quite big. In this case, the result of subtracting is the bigger number unchanged. For example, in estimating-arithmetic, if we take 30 away from 10,000, the result is 10,000 unchanged. It is this kind of subtracting that occurs when you are given a whole box of chocolates and you eat just one: almost the whole box is left. In fact, if you take out the paper wrapper and throw it away where it will not be seen, the box looks as if it had not been touched!

But when we do this kind of subtraction, we must take care not to repeat it often. It cannot be repeated and repeated without making a large difference. So we recognize a second case of subtraction in estimating-arithmetic: where the subtraction of a small number from a big one is repeated quite a number of times. In this second case, we need to estimate the total sum of all the subtracted amounts, and then subtract the total sum from the big number. It is this kind of subtraction that occurs when you go to Las Vegas and gamble small amounts each day, winding up with a net loss each day; as the days go by, your total net losses finally make a big subtraction from the fund you started out with.

A third case of subtraction in estimating-arithmetic is where two numbers are quite close to each other, or nearly equal, and one is subtracted from the other. In such a case almost all information may be lost, because we lose many significant figures. As long as we stay in estimating-arithmetic, it just is not possible to estimate reasonably the result of such a subtraction; instead, more accurate ordinary arithmetic must be used. For example:

PROBLEM 4:   John is four years old and Bill is four years old. Were they born on the same day?

Solution: The answer to this problem is *not* "four minus four equals zero; therefore there is no difference in age." "Four years old" ordinarily means "four years old on one's last birthday," and therefore one's exact age is somewhere between four years 0 days and four years and 364 days. This is true of both John and Bill. (Of course, the chance is very small [only one out of 365] that they were born on the same day.)

Answer: Very likely not.

MULTIPLICATION

Multiplication is the most important process in estimating, the commonest, and the most necessary. It is needed much more often than division and subtraction, and it often replaces the process of addition. In ordinary arithmetic, in contrast, addition is the commonest and most necessary process. Furthermore, in estimating-arithmetic, multiplication is an easy operation, since it requires not more than two significant digits; while in ordinary arithmetic, multiplication is a long and troublesome operation, often requiring five to ten significant digits.

To multiply two significant digits by two significant digits, as we do in estimating-arithmetic, there is at least one easier way that cuts down the usual mental work a great deal: this easier way is to avoid carrying digits in your head, by writing down all of what are called the "partial products." For example, suppose we multiply 97 by 56. Below, both ways are compared:

Regular Way	Easier Way
97	97
×56	×56
582	42
485	54
5432	35
	45
	5432

In the regular way, we say under our breath:

"6 times 7 is 42, put down 2 and carry the 4, 6 times 9 is 54, and 4 to carry is 58, put down 8 and carry the 5; next, 5 times 7 is 35; put down 5 and carry the 3, 5 times 9 is 45, and 3 to carry is 48, put down 8 and carry the 4."

In the "easier way," we simply write down quickly, using care to put the figures in the right places:

"6 times 7 is 42, 6 times 9 is 54, 5 times 7 is 35, 5 times 9 is 45"

and then we proceed with all the adding to be done, having all the numbers to be added presented to our gaze. This saves some mental carrying. (This so-called easier way is, of course, usable also with numbers of three or more digits to be multiplied together, but then it tends to become rather clumsy.)

For an example of multiplication in estimating-arithmetic, let's consider this problem:

PROBLEM 5:   What is the worth of a college education?

Solution: The first thing we need in order to solve this problem is some data, some raw information, to base our answer upon. From general knowledge, about which we shall have more to say later, the following assumptions may be roughly true:

a) A man who does not go to college is usually paid by the hour. He may start work at age 18 at about $1.50 an hour, wind up at age 65 at about $2.50 an hour, and earn from age 18 to 65 perhaps $2.00 an hour on the average.

b) A man who goes to college is usually paid an annual salary. He may start at age 22 at $5000 a year, wind up at age 65 at $15,000 a year, and earn perhaps $9000 a year on the average.

Accordingly, the non-college man's earnings (let us call this figure N) are:

$2.00 an hour $\times$ 40 hours a week $\times$ 50 weeks per year $\times$ 47 years,

which equals in dollars:

$2.0 \times 4.0 \times 10 \times 5.0 \times 10 \times 4.7 \times 10$

We save the three tens, and multiply successively:

$2.0 \times 4.0 = 8.0$

$8.0 \times 5.0 = 40.0$; factor out the 10, save it, and round off to 4.0;

$4.0 \times 4.7 = 18.8$; factor out the 10, save it, and round off to 1.9

So the answer N equals 1.9 times five tens (saved) multiplied together, which equals:

$1.9 \times 10 \times 10 \times 10 \times 10 \times 10 = \$190,000$

In contrast, the college man's earnings (we'll call them C) are:

$9000 a year $\times$ 43 years

which equals in dollars:

$$9.0 \times 10 \times 10 \times 10 \times 4.3 \times 10$$

We save four tens and multiply:

$9.0 \times 4.3 = 38.7$; factor out 10, save it, and round off to 3.9

So the answer C equals 3.9 times five tens (saved) multiplied together, which equals:

$$3.9 \times 10 \times 10 \times 10 \times 10 \times 10 = \$390,000$$

Now, the cost of the college education is, say, about $3000 a year for four years, or about $12,000.

Therefore, investment of about $12,000 in a college education produces a return of C minus N, $390,000 minus $190,000, or about $200,000, or more than 15 times the amount put in. (This is not a bad investment!)

We can, of course, find fault with this solution in a number of ways, just as we can find fault with any estimate. For example, the answer estimated does not take into account: the fact that money in the future is worth less than money in the present; the chances of living or dying; the general rise in prices and costs that tends to happen as years pass; and other factors. However, nearly all these factors will affect both the earnings of the non-college man and the earnings of the college man, roughly in the same proportion. So the college education is likely still to be worth more than 15 times the investment in it.

In the previous problem, we kept two significant digits at each stage in each multiplication. This is a good rule to follow in estimating-arithmetic, because if we round off to one significant digit during the process of multiplying, the result may stray considerably from the true result.

For example, in ordinary arithmetic, two times two is four. But in estimating-arithmetic, 2 stands for any number from 1.5 to 2.5. Therefore, 2 times 2 at the smallest can be 1.5 times 1.5 (which multiplies out to 2.25) and at the largest can be 2.5 times 2.5 (which multiplies out to be 6.25). So two times two, in estimating-arithmetic, when rounded off to one figure, can be 2 or 3 or 4 or 5 or 6. This is a serious degree of uncertainty – rather more uncertainty than we would care to have in most cases of estimating.

DIVISION

Division is a comparatively unusual operation, both in ordinary arithmetic and in estimating-arithmetic. Again, it is an operation that becomes a great deal easier in estimating-arithmetic; this is because two significant figures (for the dividend, the divisor, and the quotient) are all that are regularly necessary. For example:

PROBLEM 6: John Jones's income is $11,500 a year. His regular work week is 35 hours, but in the course of a year he puts in about 300 hours of overtime. About what is his hourly rate of pay?

Solution: The number of hours he works during a year is:

> 35 hours a week × 50 weeks a year, plus 300 hours, which equals 1750 plus 300, which equals 2050.

His hourly rate of pay in dollars is:

> 11500 divided by 2050

which is approximately equal to:

> (1.2 × four tens multiplied together) DIVIDED BY (2.1 × three tens multiplied together).

Canceling two ten factors on each side of the operation DIVIDED BY, we have:

> $1.2 \times 10 \times 10 \div 2.1 \times 10$

which equals $120 \div 21$.

Actually dividing:

$$
\begin{array}{r}
5.7 \\
21\overline{)120} \\
105 \\
\hline
150 \\
147 \\
\hline
3
\end{array}
$$

the result is 5.7 in dollars.

Answer: John Jones's hourly rate of pay is about $5.70.

Other Operations

Other operations, both in arithmetic and outside of it, can often be handled fairly easily by the methods of estimating. For example, let's take the operation of square root. But what is square root? Let's stop for a minute and review the meaning of square root:

The square root of a number *N* is a number *R* having the property that *R* times *R* is equal to *N*.

For example, the square root of 9 is 3, since 3 times 3 is 9. The square root of 16 is 4, since 4 times 4 equals 16. But what would be the square root of a number in between 9 and 16, such as 13?

In ordinary arithmetic, the method usually taught in school for finding square root is a long-winded affair full of rather odd rules. In fact, these rules do not have a reasonable meaning until one has obtained a good understanding of algebra. But in estimating-arithmetic, the method for finding a square root is a general common-sense method of very wide use:

Guess a reasonable value and try it. If it does not fit, then choose a more reasonable value and try that. And so on.

For example:

PROBLEM 7: A square cellar contains 13 square yards. About how long is each side?

Solution: We need to find the square root of 13. Well, the square root ought to be between 3 and 4, since 13 is between 9 and 16. The square root should be nearer to 4 than it is to 3, since 13 is nearer to 16 than it is to 9.

Suppose we try 3.8 as a possible square root for 13. Testing, 3.8 times 3.8 is equal to 14.44, which is too big. Suppose we try 3.7; 3.7 times 3.7 is 13.69, which is much closer but still too big. Suppose we try 3.6; 3.6 times 3.6 is 12.96, and this is only .04 away from 13. In fact, 12.96 rounded off is 13. So in estimating-arithmetic, we take 3.6 as the square root of 13.

Answer: Each side of the cellar is about 3.6 yards long.

How to Use One Guess to Make a Better Guess

We have just illustrated the method of:

> Guess a reasonable value and try it. If it does not fit, then choose a more reasonable value and try that. And so on.

This method of making a guess, trying it, then improving the guess, then trying that one, and so on, is a very powerful method. It has a name: the Method of Successive Approximations. People use this method often and often without realizing it:

- in finding a name in an alphabetic directory;
- in looking for a house number on a dark street;
- in learning how to play tennis; etc.

This method is the same as the Method of Trial and Error whenever each trial systematically gives you information enabling you to improve your next trial.

For example, in the square root problem above, we can summarize in Table 2 the information obtained from the first two guesses:

TABLE 2

Number of the Guess (1)	Guessed Square Root (2)	Result of Trying the Guessed Square Root (3) = (2) × (2)
1	3.8	14.44
2	3.7	13.69
Difference	0.1	0.75

We can see that a decrease of 0.1 in the guess produced a decrease of 0.75 in the result—which is about seven times as much. Now we want to change the result from 13.69 (the result of the last guess) to 13.00 (the number we are trying to find the square root of). This is a decrease in the result of 0.69. So it seems clear that a decrease in the second guess 3.7 amounting to 0.1 (approximately a seventh of 0.69) ought to be just about right. And of course it is, for the third guess 3.6 produces a result of 12.96, which is very close to the desired 13.00.

How to Choose the Data to Start With

As we said above, estimating consists of two processes — the process of reasoning mathematically in order to calculate approximately, and the process of choosing the data or information to start the estimate with, the observations and facts which we base the estimate on.

To choose the data for starting an estimate, it is useful to know many pieces of information about the world. Unfortunately this takes wide experience which most of us do not have. So for anchoring our estimates we fall back upon almanacs, directories, reference books, and tables of statistics.

For example, for estimating distances, it is useful to know a group of distances such as the following:

New York to Boston:	200 miles
San Francisco to New York:	2500 miles
diameter of the earth:	8000 miles
earth to the moon, average	240,000 miles
earth to the sun, average	93 million miles
sun to the outermost planet (Pluto), average	3.7 billion miles
sun to the nearest star (Alpha Centauri)	4.3 light-years*
thickness of the disk of our galaxy, central part	about 8000 light-years
diameter of the disk of our galaxy	about 80,000 light-years
distance to the farthest observed celestial objects	about 6 billion light-years

---

*   A light-year is the distance light travels in a year—about 5.9 million million miles.

For making estimates, we need to keep our eyes and ears open from day to day, to notice data and facts which are useful for drawing conclusions and making estimates. How fast do trains usually travel? How many weeks a year does a man usually work? How many pages are there in an ordinary novel? How many words are there on an ordinary page? The answers to these questions and many more like them provide benchmarks for surveying, cornerstones for good judgments, and data for estimating.

The Long Reach of Estimating

7

WITH THIS SURVEY of the operations of estimating-arithmetic behind us, we know what estimating-arithmetic essentially amounts to:

- calculating with one or two significant digits; and
- always calculating in the easiest way that is still likely to give a reasonable answer;

for, after all, the answer is to be rough and approximate.

Let us now take a look at a number of problems and solutions that involve estimating, and that show its long reach and wide applicability. Some of these problems are practical now; others might be practical 200 years from now—if then!

A Light-Year in Miles

PROBLEM 1:   For measuring distances between the stars, a unit often used is the light-year, the distance that light will travel in a year. How long is a light-year?

Solution: A light-year is the distance that light will travel in a year. Light travels at the rate of 186,324 miles a second; this fact may be looked up in a physics book, dictionary, encyclopedia, or almanac.

The distance that light travels in a year is therefore:

186,324 miles/second × 60 seconds/minute × 60 minutes/hour × 24 hours/day × 365 days/year.

Of course we do not want to multiply out all these numbers using ordinary arithmetic. So we replace them where necessary by numbers of one or two significant digits times factors of ten multiplied together:

Replace 186,324 by 190,000, and this by 1.9 × 10 × 10 × 10 × 10 × 10

Replace 365 by 370, and this by 3.7 × 10 × 10

Then a light-year in miles is equal to:

1.9 × 10 × 10 × 10 × 10 × 10 × 6.0 × 10 × 6.0 × 10 × 2.4 × 10 × 3.7 × 10 × 10

Collecting the tens, $5 + 1 + 1 + 1 + 2 =$ ten 10's. So this is equal to:

1.9 × 6.0 × 6.0 × 2.4 × 3.7 × ten 10's multiplied together.

Proceeding with the various steps:

1.9 × 6.0 = 11.4 = 1.1 × 10 − save another 10;

1.1 × 6.0 = 6.6;

6.6 × 2.4 = 15.84 = 1.6 times 10 − save another 10;

1.6 × 3.7 = 5.92 = 5.9

The total number of tens occurring is 12. Therefore, a light-year in miles is 5.9 times 12 tens multiplied together, or about 5.9 million million miles, approximately 6 trillion miles.

How to Deal with Very Big Numbers: Powers

In order to deal with very big numbers, such as the number of miles in a light-year, we need a neat and convenient way to designate a number of tens multiplied together. To keep track of tens multiplied together, mathematicians use a small number written in the upper right-hand corner of a number, which is called a *power* or an *exponent*. For example, 10 times 10 times 10 times 10 times 10, which is five tens multiplied together, is written 10^5 and this is read as "ten to the fifth power," or "ten to the exponent 5" or briefly as "ten to the fifth." In ordinary language, this number is a hundred thousand, 100,000. And similarly for any other number of tens multiplied together.

Thus a million is 10^6 (ten to the sixth). A billion is 10^9 (ten to the ninth). And a trillion is 10^{12} (ten to the 12th).

A much bigger number is ten to the hundredth power, 10^{100}; in ordinary arithmetic this would have to be written as the figure 1 with one hundred figure 0's following it. This number is a "googol." The word was coined in the late 1930's by a young nephew of Dr. Edward Kasner, co-author of *Mathematics and the Imagination*; the word has become accepted and can be found in the dictionary.

Using the power or exponent way of denoting very big numbers, a light-year is 5.9×10^{12} miles (read "five point nine times ten to the twelfth miles").

The same system for counting a number of equal factors all multiplied together may be used for other numbers than ten. Two to the 5th power is $2 \times 2 \times 2 \times 2 \times 2 = 32$. Two to the 10th power is $2 \times 2 \times 2 \times 2 \times 2 \times 2 \times 2 \times 2 \times 2 \times 2 = 32 \times 32 = 1024$. Three to the 4th power is $3 \times 3 \times 3 \times 3 = 81$.

Special names are very often used for powers 2 and 3. 10^2 is regularly called "ten squared," instead of "ten to the second power." 10^3 is regularly called "ten cubed," instead of "ten to the third power."

Traveling to the Nearest Star

PROBLEM 2: How far away in miles is the nearest star (not our sun)?

Solution: The nearest star is Alpha Centauri. This star is 4.3 light-years away. (Information from an astronomy textbook or an almanac.)

The number of miles corresponding to 4.3 light-years is:

4.3 light-years $\times 5.9 \times 10^{12}$ miles/light-year

This is equal to:

$10^{12} \times (4.3 \times 5.9 = 25.37 = 2.5 \times 10)$

which is equal to:

$$2.5 \times 10^{13}$$

So the nearest star is 2.5 times 10^{13} miles away, or 25 million million miles.

PROBLEM 3: Will man ever be able to travel to the nearest star?

Solution: This problem cannot be answered when stated in this way because of the word "ever," which covers an unlimited amount of time. But it can be partially answered.

The distance to the nearest star Alpha Centauri is about 2.5×10^{13} miles.

A representative speed which man has so far attained in artificial satellites and planetary probes is about 7 miles per second. If this speed could be maintained for a year, the distance D that would be traveled would be:

7 miles/second × 60 seconds/minute × 60 minutes/ hour × 24 hours/day × 365 days/year

A figure which we shall clearly need for problems of this general nature is the number of seconds in a year. Let's take time out and calculate it once and for all.

PROBLEM 4: What is the number of seconds in a year?

Solution: The number of seconds in a year is:

60 sec/min × 60 min/hr × 24 hr/day × 365 days/yr

This number is equal to:

$$6.0 \times 10 \times 6.0 \times 10 \times 2.4 \times 10 \times 3.7 \times 10^2$$

Saving 10^5 and proceeding with the various steps:

$6.0 \times 6.0 = 36.0 \times 10 -$ save the 10;

$3.6 \times 2.4 = 8.64 = 8.6$;

$8.6 \times 3.7 = 31.82 = 3.2 \times 10 -$ save another 10

The total number of 10's is $5 + 1 + 1$, or 7 in all. So the number of seconds in a year is 3.2×10^7, or about 30 million. (If accurately calculated for a year of $365\frac{1}{4}$ days, it is 3.15576×10^7.)

Returning now to the prior problem:

Solution to Problem 3 (continued): If one traveled at 7 miles a second for a year, the distance traveled would be:

$$7 \text{ mi/sec} \times 3.2 \times 10^7 \text{ sec/yr} = 22.4 \times 10^7 \text{ miles} = 2.2 \times 10^8$$

miles, or about 200 million miles.

Suppose that man in the future could eventually travel 100 times as fast, in empty space between the stars. This would be a distance traveled of 2.2×10^{10} miles in a year.

Divide this distance into the distance of 2.5×10^{13} miles to the nearest star; the answer is 1.1×10^3, or 1100. So it would take about 1100 years to make the trip one way. Suppose there are three human generations to the century; then, about 33 generations after starting, the descendants of the original crew might be approaching the nearest star!

Actually, a number of factors have been neglected in this estimate of the solution, some of them favorable, some of them unfavorable. One of the favorable factors is that there would be almost no resistance to travel through space, and any acceleration gained in any way would be a lasting help in making the journey. One of the unfavorable factors is that according to the Einstein theory of relativity no material thing can travel faster than the speed of light, 186, 324 miles a second. Further, it would take a huge amount of energy to get any large object up to any large fraction of the speed of light.

How Much Can One Do in a Lifetime?

PROBLEM 5:   Laura Berkeley, age 12, and I were talking one day about counting. She said "Sometimes I count while waiting to fall asleep. I am going to count to a googol before I die." I said, "If you spent all your waking life counting, you would never get that far." What are the facts?

Solution: The fastest that a human being can choose to perform any action is about 6 to 8 actions per second, such as counting numbers (if they are small ones), striking keys on a typewriter, etc.

So let us ask the equivalent question "About how many conscious actions can a human being carry out in a lifetime?" Suppose that we let him sleep only 7 hours a night, that he stays alive for 90 years, and that his childhood and his old age are just as efficient as the prime of life.

Then the number N of possible conscious actions is about:

> 7 actions/second $\times$ 17/24 (which is the fraction of the day spent in activity) $\times$ 3.2 $\times$ 10^7 seconds/year (which is the number of seconds in a year—see Problem 4, page 97) $\times$ 90 years/lifetime

This is equal to:

> $7 \times 17/24 \times 3.2 \times 10^7 \times 9.0 \times 10$

Saving out 10^8 and calculating the rest:

> $7 \times .71 = 4.97 = 5.0$
> $5.0 \times 3.2 = 16.0 = 1.6 \times 10$—save another 10;
> $1.6 \times 9.0 = 14.4 = 1.4 \times 10$—save another 10

The result is 1.4×10^{10}. Let us round it off high, since we are looking for a maximum. The answer is 10^{11}, a hundred billion.

In other words, the best a human being can hope for during his waking lifetime is to choose to do about a hundred billion actions, probably much less. So if all Laura's waking lifetime were spent counting one by one, she might get as far as a hundred billion, 1 with 11 zeros after it. But a googol is 10^{100}, 1 with a hundred zeros after it, and would be unattainable.

If the Earth Were All Sand . . .

PROBLEM 6: Michel Chalufour, age seven, came to me one day with this problem. "If the earth were all sand, how many grains of sand would there be?"

Solution: We need a fair amount of data to solve this problem.

1) How big is sand? By looking in a geology textbook we find that the dimension of the finest sand is about 400 grains to an inch of length.

2) How big is the earth? By looking in a geography, we find that the radius of the earth, the distance from the center to the surface, is quite close to 4000 miles (actually it is a little less).

3) Since the shape of the earth is approximately a round ball or sphere, how do we compute the volume of a sphere? By looking in a school arithmetic book we find the formula for the volume of a sphere:

4/3 times Pi times the radius cubed.

To cube a number means to multiply 1 by the number three times; for example, 10^3 is $1 \times 10 \times 10 \times 10$. The constant Pi is about 3.14.

4) To go from inches to miles, we make use of:

12 inches make a foot;

5280 feet make a mile.

In order to combine the data we need to multiply:

(number of grains of sand per cubic inch) × (number of cubic inches in a cubic foot) × (number of cubic feet in a cubic mile) × (number of cubic miles in the volume of the earth)

So the answer to Michel's question is:

$A = (400)^3$ grains/cu. in. × $(12)^3$ cu. in./cu. ft. × $(5280)^3$ cu. ft./cu. mi. × $4/3 \times 3.14 \times (4000)^3$ cu. mi.

$A = (4 \times 10^2)^3 \times (1.2 \times 10)^3 \times (5.3 \times 10^3)^3 \times 1.3 \times 3.1 \times (4 \times 10^3)^3$

$A = 4^3 \times 10^6 \times 1.2^3 \times 10^3 \times 5.3^3 \times 10^9 \times 1.3 \times 3.1 \times 4^3 \times 10^9$

Now, $4^3 = 6.4 \times 10$, $(1.2)^3 = 1.7$, and $(5.3)^3 = 1.5 \times 10^2$, as may be found by multiplying out. Therefore:

$A = 6.4 \times 10 \times 10^6 \times 1.7 \times 10^3 \times 1.5 \times 10^2 \times 10^9 \times 1.3 \times 3.1 \times 6.4 \times 10 \times 10^9$.

$6.4 \times 1.7 = 10.9 = 1.1 \times 10 -$ save another 10

$1.1 \times 1.5 = 1.7$
$1.7 \times 1.3 = 2.2$
$2.2 \times 3.1 = 6.8$
$6.8 \times 6.4 = 43.5 = 4.4 \times 10 -$ save another 10

The number of powers of 10 is $1 + 6 + 3 + 2 + 9 + 1 + 9 + 1 + 1$, or 33.

So the answer to Michel's problem is about 4.4×10^{33}, or, since the sand might be a little coarser than 400 grains to the inch, let us say 10^{33}. Thus, if the earth were all sand, the number of grains of sand would be about 10^{33}.

This means of course that the number of all the grains of sand on all the beaches, shores, and deserts of the earth is a very much smaller figure. In fact, we could estimate it!

This problem leads us to the following question:

> If all the universe that we know of were filled completely with the smallest particles we know of, how many would there be?

And here we need a neat and convenient way to deal with small numbers.

How to Deal with Very Small Numbers: Negative Powers

In order to deal with very small numbers, such as "the size of the smallest particles that we know of," we need a convenient way to designate the result by dividing one by a number of tens multiplied together. For this purpose, mathematicians use a power (or an exponent) with a *minus sign* (−) in front of it. For example, one hundredth (1/100) is written 10^{-2}, (read "ten to the minus two") and one millionth is written 10^{-6}, (read "ten to the minus six"), and so on. This minus sign makes the power a negative number instead of a positive number; the meaning of a negative number is that the direction of counting or measuring is the opposite from the direction of counting or measuring a positive number. A temperature of minus eight degrees is eight degrees below zero temperature; a temperature of eight (or plus eight) degrees is eight degrees above zero. A bank balance of minus $30 is a balance where you have *overdrawn* your bank account by $30, a deficit.

Very small numbers are neatly handled with negative exponents. For example, 10^{-33} would be the fraction of the volume of the earth occupied by one grain of fine sand.

Now that we have positive exponents, as in 10^3, meaning a thousand, and negative exponents, as in 10^{-4}, meaning one ten-thousandth, what is the meaning we should attach to ten to the zero power, 10^0? Ten to the zero power, 10^0, is equal to 1. Why? Here is the pattern of the reasoning: If we multiply 10^3 by 10^4, we obtain 10^7, because if three tens multiplied together are multiplied by four tens multiplied together, we obtain seven tens multiplied together:

$$(10 \times 10 \times 10) \times (10 \times 10 \times 10 \times 10) = (10 \times 10 \times 10 \times 10 \times 10 \times 10 \times 10)$$

So multiplying two powers together is accomplished by adding their exponents:

$$10^3 \times 10^4 = 10^{3+4} = 10^7$$

Now if three tens multiplied together (10^3, one thousand) are multiplied by one divided by three tens multiplied together (10^{-3}, one thousandth), we obtain 1:

$$10^3 \times 10^{-3} = 1$$

Multiplying by adding exponents we have the same result:

$$10^3 \times 10^{-3} = 10^{3-3} = 10^0 = 1$$

This argument is not a proof: it simply shows a sketch of a proof, and shows that our statements are reasonable to believe, are plausible.

If the Universe Were Filled with the Tiniest Particles

With this preparation we are ready for the following problem.

PROBLEM 7: If all the universe that we know of were filled completely (packed solid) with the smallest particles that we know of, how many would there be?

Solution:

Part 1 — Data:

1) Apparently the smallest well-established particle that scientists know of at the present is the proton, which has a diameter of approximately 10^{-13} centimeters.
2) There are about 2.54 centimeters to the inch.
3) The farthest distance that has currently been observed with telescopes is about 6×10^9 light-years in any direction from the earth.

Part 2 — Combining the Data:

So the desired number N is the cube of:

10^{13} protons/centimeter $\times$ 2.54 centimeters/inch $\times$ 12 inches/foot $\times$ 5280 feet/mile $\times$ 5.9×10^{12} miles/light-year $\times 6 \times 10^9$ light-years $\times$ 2 (opposite directions from the earth)

We might call this number L, for it is the number of protons (packed right next to each other) that would lie in a straight line from one side to the other side of the currently observed universe.

$L = 10^{13} \times 2.5 \times 1.2 \times 10 \times 5.3 \times 10^3 \times 5.9 \times 10^{12} \times 6 \times 10^9 \times 2$

$2.5 \times 1.2 = 3.0;$

$3.0 \times 5.3 = 15.9 = 1.6 \times 10 -$ save another 10;

$1.6 \times 5.9 = 9.4;$

$9.4 \times 6.0 = 56.4 = 5.6 \times 10 -$ save another 10;

$5.6 \times 2.0 = 11.2 = 1.1 \times 10 -$ save another 10

The number of tens comes to: $13 + 1 + 3 + 12 + 9 + 1 + 1 + 1 = 41$.

So, $L = 1.1 \times 10^{41}$. So, $N = L \times L \times L = 1.1 \times 1.1 \times 1.1 \times 10^{123} = 1.3 \times 10^{123}$

At least one conclusion can be drawn from this calculation that tends to comfort those minds like my own which prefer finite numbers to infinite ones. Mathematicians talk about "infinity," which has several meanings; one of these is the "number" that is approached as you divide one successively by a thousandth, a millionth, a billionth, and so on until your divisor is indistinguishably close to zero. Well, if you tried to use all of the smallest particles in the known universe as figures "0" to write infinity in Arabic numerals, starting 1,000,000,000, . . . you would still never succeed, for infinity is infinitely larger than 10^{123}.

The Number of People the Earth Can Support

PROBLEM 8:   How many people can the earth support?

Solution: From one point of view it is hardly possible to solve this problem because we do not know what the future will bring forth as inventions and techniques to support human life. But nevertheless, let's make some not too unreasonable assumptions and make at least some kind of estimate. As more information becomes available, the estimate can be revised.

Part 1 — Data:

a) Suppose that eventually a plot of fertile land 100 feet by 100 feet will support one person.

b) Suppose that eventually 70 percent of the land of the earth can become fertile.

c) The earth's surface is 3/4 water and 1/4 land, according to a geography textbook.

d) The surface of a sphere, according to the formula in a school arithmetic book, is 4 times Pi times the Radius squared.

Part 2 — Combining the Data:

The number of people N that the earth can support is $N =$ (the surface of the earth in square miles) TIMES (number of square feet in a square mile) TIMES (1/4, which is land) TIMES (70 percent, which is fertile) DIVIDED BY (the allowance of 10,000 square feet of land for a person).

$N = 4 \times 3.14 \times (4000)^2$ earth's surface in square miles $\times$ $(5280)^2$ square feet/square mile $\times$ .25 land/surface $\times$ 0.7 fertile land/all land $\div$ 10,000 square feet of land allowance for one person.

We change .25 to 2.5×10^{-1} and 0.7 to 7.0×10^{-1} to put them in the standard style. And $\div$ 10,000 is the same as $\times 10^{-4}$.

$N = 4 \times 3.1 \times 4.0^2 \times 10^6 \times 5.3^2 \times 10^6 \times 2.5 \times 10^{-1} \times 7.0 \times 10^{-1} \times 10^{-4}$

So:

$4 \times 3.1 = 12.4 = 1.2 \times 10$ — save another 10;

$1.2 \times 4.0 = 4.8$;

$4.8 \times 4.0 = 19.2 = 1.9 \times 10$ — save another 10;

$1.9 \times 5.3 = 10.1 = 1.0 \times 10$ — save another 10;

$1.0 \times 5.3 = 5.3$;

$5.3 \times 2.5 = 13.3 = 1.3 \times 10$ — save another 10;

$1.3 \times 7.0 = 9.1$

The number of tens is: $6 + 6 - 1 - 1 - 4 + 4 = 10$

So $N = 9.1 \times 10^{10}$, or about 90 billion.

Answer: Under these assumptions, the earth could support a maximum population of about 90 billion people.

This leads us to the next problem.

PROBLEM 9:   How soon will the problem of what to do about the increase of people have to be solved?

Solution:

Part 1 — Data:

a) In 1900 the world had 1.6 billion people.

b) In 1950 it had about 2.4 billion people.

c) In 1965 the world had about 3.0 billion people.

Part 2 — Combining the Data:

a) Since the population of the world increased by 50 percent in the half century from 1900 to 1950, let us estimate that population doubles each century.

b) Then in 4 centuries the population will increase 16 times, and in 5 centuries it will increase 32 times.

c) Dividing 3 billion into 90 billion, we obtain a possible increase of 30 times.

Answer: Under these assumptions, then, in slightly less

than five centuries, the problem of the increase of population will have to be solved.

This answer of course depends on the rate of doubling.

If doubling of population under present conditions should turn out to be at the rate say of once in 60 years instead of once a century, then the time for five doublings is 300 instead of 500 years, and a little less than 300 years is the time available for solving the problem.

Some Conclusions

Enough has been said perhaps to show the great power and the essential simplicity of the arithmetic of estimating. Of course, the solutions to the problems given here can be refined in several ways; for instance, more accurate data can be used in the solution. For example, in Problem 9, the 10,000-square-foot allowance of fertile land to support one person should most certainly be much more carefully estimated.

In reality, however, there is now so much information available in standard reference books and in the ordinary experience of ordinary people, that when this information is combined with the methods of estimating explained in this part of the book, a great deal of useful, interesting, and exciting information can be calculated, and calculated easily — even if "roughly and approximately."

Estimating, and Being Right

PROBABLY THE MOST IMPORTANT of all applications of the art of estimating is in being right—achieving correctness —making certain the proposed answer to some problem "is in the right ball park."

Over and over again people tell you a figure that is wrong. Your trained habits of questioning a figure and estimating approximately what it ought to be enables you to catch many errors almost as soon as you see a figure. As you look at it, you say to yourself: Why is this figure so big? It looks much bigger than I thought it would be.

Or you say to yourself: Why is this figure so small? It looks much smaller than I thought it would be.

In order to make this kind of prompt judgment, it is useful, before you look at the figure, to construct in your mind a rough estimate of the size that the figure should be. Then when you see the figure, you already have another number to compare with it.

We shall now give examples of several kinds of errors and discuss some of their causes and cures. Then at the end of the chapter we shall try to express some general rules for helping us to make sure that a proposed answer to a problem "is in the right ball park."

Missing Zeros or Extra Zeros

A rather common kind of mistake, especially in newspaper reports, is to leave off zeros from a figure, or to add zeros on to it. For example:

PROBLEM 1:   Here are three headlines:
  a) "15,000 in Graduating Class of Scottsville High School Receive Diplomas"
  b) "1500 in Graduating Class of Teterboro High School Receive Diplomas"
  c) "150 in Graduating Class of Underwood High School Receive Diplomas"

Suppose you know that the population of each of these three residential communities is about 90,000. Which headlines are CERTAINLY wrong?

Solution: A graduating class in a public high school in a residential community of 90,000 will usually consist of almost all (say 95 percent) of the young people of about age 18 in a community. Of course, ages of people in a community may vary all the way from 0 to over 95; but there are many more at younger ages; so young people at age 18 may be, say, 1/60 of the community. So, estimating,

95% of 1/60 of 90,000 is between 1400 and 1500.

Therefore, headlines (*a*) and (*c*) are certainly wrong, while headline (*b*) is quite likely to be right.

This kind of error, because of its magnitude, can be caught fairly easily by a little reflection and some estimating.

Adding Instead of Subtracting, or Vice Versa

Every now and then an error occurs because something is added when it should be subtracted, or vice versa.

PROBLEM 2:   The Jurgen Company, Boston, Massachusetts, received an order from Mr. H. G. Tarbell, New London,

Ontario, Canada, for a scientific kit, together with a check for $22.75 in Canadian money. The company reported that it could not fill the order right away since the kit was currently out of stock; Mr. Tarbell wrote that he wanted his money back.

The assistant bookkeeper made out the refund check in U.S. money first for $22.75. This error was caught, because Canadian dollars are not the same as American dollars, and it was sent back to her for correction.

Then she made out a check for $24.57. Was this right?

Solution: At the time of the problem, United States dollars were worth more than Canadian dollars. Therefore, $22.75 in Canadian money had to be a smaller amount in U.S. money.

The assistant bookkeeper insisted at first that the discount was 8 percent and that she had correctly calculated that 8 percent of $22.75 was $1.82. But finally she saw that the discount should be subtracted from the $22.75, to represent the United States dollars, and the check in U.S. dollars should have been made out for $20.93.

This kind of error can be caught by estimating whether the answer will be bigger than some starting figure, or smaller.

Confirming by Estimating Indirectly

The following true story came from a friend of mine (names have been changed).

PROBLEM 3: The other day we made a proposal to Mr. Samuel Smith of Argus Corp. In that proposal we estimated there were about 23,000 installations of punch-card machines in the United States. He promptly said that that figure was too small—that there were about 100,000 installations. Which of us was right?

Solution: Well, I asked him:

"What percentage of installations are leased?"

We agreed almost all, say 95 percent. I asked him:

"What is the average value of equipment at a punch-card installation?"

After some figuring together, we came up with $87,000. Now, we both knew the standard ratio of monthly income to purchase price, which is 1 to 70. So the rental from an average installation for a year would be:

1/70 of $87,000 times 12 or about $15,000

So the total amount of annual rental which manufacturers would receive from punch card installations, if there were 100,000, would be:

95 percent times $15,000 times 100,000, or about $1.4 billion

but only about a quarter of that, if the number of installations were 23,000.

Now we both knew that the $1.4 billion a year was clearly three or more times the maximum amount of rental income possible.

So Mr. Smith quickly conceded that his estimate of 100,000 was too high, and he agreed that ours seemed to be right.

This kind of avoidance of error is a good example of confirming a figure by using a second method of estimating it.

How Correct Figures Are Calculated in a Well-Run Organization

In a careful well-run organization such as the home office of a life insurance company, the regular procedure for calculations (when human beings do the calculating) is well worked out and remarkably careful. The procedure usually is much like the following:

1) To prepare a sheet of figures, such as premium rates for a new insurance policy for each age from 20 to 65, say, the calculation is done first by one clerk, who is called the "first worker." Using a desk calculating machine, he calculates the new premium separately for each age, applying the formula he is given; when the sheet is finished, the first worker writes his initials on it.

2) The calculation sheet is then given to a second, more experienced clerk, who is called the "second worker." He repeats the calculation for each age and places a centered pencil dot next to each figure he agrees with. He puts a light penciled X next to each figure that he disagrees with. When the second worker finishes the sheet, he gives it back to the first worker to make corrections.

3) The first worker calculates once more each figure that has been questioned, changes any figure that he finds is wrong, and gives the sheet again to the second worker. If a figure is now right, the second worker erases the penciled X next to it and dots the figure; if any figure is still not right, according to the second worker's views, he leaves the X, and returns the sheet to the first worker for additional correction.

4) After the first worker and second worker have finally agreed through independent calculations of each figure, the second worker writes his initials on the sheet; and he gives it to a still more experienced, third person, such as the assistant section head, who is called the "inspector."

5) The inspector first "spot-checks" the calculation. He chooses at random several sample figures, and he recomputes each one to satisfy himself that it is right. It is not expected and not desired that the inspector recompute every figure.

6) If all his "spot-checks" verify, then he looks over the entire sheet of results and applies the following questions:

- Are the figures reasonable?
- Are the figures consistent? Do they change from one age to another by reasonable differences?
- Has the right source data or information been used?
- How do the figures compare with prior figures? the figures for last year? the figures the last time the calculation was made? etc.
- Has anything been left out that should go in?
- Has anything been put in that should be left out?
- Does the description written on the sheet specify precisely what the figures are?
- Is the sheet properly dated, initialed, and numbered?
- Has the calculation been made exactly in accordance with the instructions given?

If the inspector is satisfied with the answer as he determines it for each one of these questions (and any other reasonable questions that he thinks should be applied), then he also writes his initials on the sheet and the sheet is accepted as being correct.

How can errors pass through such a careful process as this? They can and they do.

Momentary Inattention from the Second Worker

Sometimes the second worker has a moment of inattention, and he puts a dot next to a figure that the first worker has calculated incorrectly. Inspection cannot always catch these errors. Instead, if and when they are found later by accident, the second worker is reprimanded—but in the absence of finding them, of course, no reprimand occurs. Furthermore, no reprimand can affect past errors that were not caught. The process of inspection by the third worker does not usually catch an isolated error like 193.67 in place of 193.07.

To deal with this kind of error, if there is much evidence that the second worker is inattentive and careless, about the only useful procedure is to change to another clerk who is more attentive and careful.

Obscurely Written Figures

Often one of the digits in a number is written carelessly. For example, a zero [0] may be written with an opening at the top which makes it look a little like a six [6]. Or a nine [9] may be written with an opening at the top that makes it look a little like a four [4].

One invariable rule in business is to write all figures clearly; another is to avoid typed strikeovers of figures, because of the difficulty in deciphering these. Yet even well-trained people sometimes neglect or forget these rules.

Misreading a figure is the kind of mistake that can slip by both a first worker and a second worker, because each one treats the ambiguous digit as expressing what he means, and each worker may have a different interpretation. This kind of error can be reduced by always insisting that every digit be written with the utmost clarity.

Use of the Wrong Starting Data

Sometimes the wrong table of original data is selected with which to make the calculation. For example, in a life insurance company the premium rates for males and the premium rates for females may differ a little, because females live longer—by about five years on the average. Therefore the original tables of figures for females from which premium rates are calculated differ from the original tables for males. A possible error, therefore, is the use of original tables for females when male rates are to be calculated, and vice versa. This is a kind of error which can slip through both first worker and second worker, and which the inspector must catch. It is his fault if this kind of error finally slips through.

This kind of error—use of the wrong starting data—is

common and is deeply ingrained in human nature. It causes many answers to many problems to be worthless. The situation is simple when there are only two alternatives, such as the rates for males and the rates for females as in the example above. In such a case, the error can be caught by calculating independently a premium rate at a given age on the basis of the male rates and on the basis of the female rates, and then comparing these two figures with the corresponding calculated premium rates in the table. But in the general situation, to change from the wrong starting data to the right starting data may take a great deal of thoughtful analysis, effort, and deliberate counteraction of human nature.

Omission of a Portion of a Cost

Another kind of error can occur in calculating the cost of manufacturing a product—this is the omission of some significant portion of the cost. For example, suppose we have to calculate the cost of manufacturing 5000 kits where each kit uses 30 kinds of parts, and the specified number of each kind of part for each kit ranges from one to 200. When determining the cost of the kit, we can obtain correct prices from all the suppliers, multiply by the correct quantities per kit, divide by 5000, and determine the actual unit kit cost.

Yet when all the kits are completed, it may be found that many of the suppliers delivered 5 to 10 percent more than what was ordered, and they have to be paid for the overage; and so the actual materials cost of the kit rises by, say 3 percent, because more materials were delivered than could be used in the completed 5000 kits.

This kind of error can be caught by enumerating ahead of time *all* the portions of a cost as imaginatively as possible and estimating the relative effect of variation in each portion of a cost on the total cost.

Mistakes That Occur in Reports

Another kind of error results from the process of repeating information from other sources. Often a writer unintentionally changes slightly a fact or a meaning in the course of writing or reporting on some subject. Human beings seem unable to be completely accurate in either talking or writing. For example, in the book *Education and Freedom* by Vice Admiral H. G. Rickover, published by E. P. Dutton and Co., 1959, the following two paragraphs occur at the start of Chapter 4 "The Meaning of a Profession" (page 61):

> To practice a profession one must have acquired mastery of an academic discipline as well as a technique for applying this special knowledge to the problems of everyday life. A profession is therefore intellectual in content, practical in application.
>
> The first definition of the term I could find goes back to the time of the Renaissance when Europe's universities became in essence training schools for professional men. The Oxford English Dictionary of 1541 says that a profession is "a vocation in which a professed knowledge of some department of learning or science is used in its application to the affairs of others."

PROBLEM 4: Is there any error in this passage? Can it be removed?

Solution: The date 1541 seems unreasonable. It seems too early historically for Oxford University in England to have issued a dictionary. Also the definition quoted seems to be more modern in tone and phrasing than is likely for something supposedly written over 400 years ago.

References tell us that the first renowned English dictionary was the dictionary of Samuel Johnson published about 1746. The Encyclopaedia Britannica (11th edition) lists the first dictionary in English as appearing in 1623. Referring to the Shorter Oxford English Dictionary (first published in 1933, reprinted 1947 with corrections), we do find the definition just as stated by Rickover. Following that, we find the remark: "Applied specifically to the three learned professions of divinity, law, and medicine; also to the military profession. 1541." This remark shows that the first use of the word "profession" (in this sense) as determined by the dictionary makers was apparently in 1541.

Thus we find the mistake that did occur, and that could have been caught by the habit of estimating numbers.

The wording could be corrected to read:

> The Oxford English Dictionary indicates that as long ago as 1541 the word "profession" was in use meaning "a vocation in which a professed knowledge of some department of learning or science is used in its application to the affairs of others."

To deal with errors of this kind, the only feasible procedure is to expect them from time to time, and to be prepared to catch them.

A Mistake That Actually Occurred in a Business

We shall close our illustrations of errors with two startling ones that actually occurred in small businesses. Here is the first (the name and product line of the business are changed):

PROBLEM 5:   In the Dresden Company, makers of furniture, the bookkeeper keeps a summary of each page of the record of deposits and checks. Table 1 shows the summary for May 1966, reporting:

- in Column (1), the number of the page in the record of bank deposits and checks;
- in Column (2), the total of checks entered;
- in Column (3), the total of deposits made;
- in Column (4), the net effect of that page's transactions, that is, the difference between total deposits and total checks;
- in Column (5), the cumulative net effect or balance brought forward from one page to the next.

TABLE 1

Dresden Co. — Deposit and Check Record Summary for May 1966

(1) Page	(2) Checks (Minus)	(3) Deposits (Plus)	(4) Net	(5) Cumulative Net
				+10534.49 (at beginning of month)
1	833.37	1403.57	+570.20	+11104.69
2	1593.70	1034.15	−559.55	+10545.14
3	523.28	0	−523.28	+10021.86
4	372.02	634.31	+262.29	+10284.15
5	4097.47	2723.78	−1373.69	+8910.46
6	938.88	5849.06	−4910.18	+4000.28
7	2926.94	3248.91	+321.97	+4322.25
8	3322.53	0	−3322.53	+999.72
9	16.00	0	−16.00	+983.72 (at end of month)

Is there any error in Table 1?

Solution: The balance in the fund at the start of the month is about $10,000. The amount at the end of the month is about $900. This is a tremendous change.

Let's look at the net for each page. The net for page 1, plus 1400 minus 800 is about plus 600 — OK. For page 2, minus 1500 plus 1000 is about minus 500 — OK. Similarly for pages 3, 4, and 5. But for page 6, we have minus 900 plus 5800, and the net is given as minus 4900. This should be plus 4900. Here is a huge error. For pages 7, 8, and 9 the figures appear about right. The cumulative net after page 6 in Column (5) apparently should be 8910.46 plus 4910.18 (about 14,000). The cumulative net at the end of the month should be about 10,800, not about 980.

Why did this error occur? Because the figures were not inspected.

Another Mistake That Actually Occurred in a Business

Some mistakes are so dreadful that when they happen they are remembered for months and months. This one occurred in a business that we shall call Fallon Corporation. Here is the situation, expressed as a problem.

PROBLEM 6: The fiscal year for Fallon Corporation ends on August 31. During September 1966 an important conference was scheduled; Mr. Fallon asked Mrs. Schwarz (the bookkeeper, who had been with the firm about eight years) to put together the annual operating figures for the 12 months ending August 31, 1966. She compiled each set of figures in a two-way table (see Table 2). Using an adding machine, she added the annual figures for each kind of income or expense to get a grand total for the year. She also added the total figures for each month to get a grand total for the year. The two grand total figures for income agreed to the penny; so did the expenses. She gave the sheets to Mr. Fallon. He received the sheets in the last few minutes before the meeting, went into the meeting, and started to show them. Immediately he saw there was something wrong.

What was it?

Solution: Income is reported as about $194,000. Expenses are reported as about $95,000. This indicates that profit was about $100,000, more than half of the gross income! This is so extraordinary as to be almost certainly false.

Looking over the column of monthly total expense, we see that each figure is over 10,000; so the annual total for 12 months must be over 120,000. Perhaps the 1 for 100,000 has disappeared. Also, apparently, the 1 for 100,000 has disappeared from the annual total for materials. Because of two errors that compensated each other, the cross-check of annual total appeared to be verified!

How could this error occur?

TABLE 2

Fallon Corporation — Annual Income and Expenses, Fiscal Year Ending Aug. 31, 1966

Income

	From: Magazine	Publications	Kits	Royalties	Miscellaneous	Monthly Total
1965						
Sept	11412.40	831.40	175.95	0	27.00	12446.75
Oct	10158.24	84.09	4768.85	0	12.60	15023.78
Nov	14152.34	846.53	270.99	0	56.90	15326.76
Dec	11839.68	258.89	7966.73	0	6.00	20071.30
1966						
Jan	14099.21	49.21	532.92	0	6.00	14687.34
Feb	10196.22	47.12	6504.89	214.56	5.35	16968.14
Mar	19160.86	108.52	382.11	206.95	2.50	19860.94
Apr	17209.46	27.48	339.62	3125.00	0	20701.56
May	14409.45	1186.77	247.45	300.70	0	16144.37
June	10813.82	677.75	92.42	0	4.40	11588.39
July	16120.86	62.57	252.31	0	0	16435.74
Aug	13959.79	62.66	141.99	260.69	157.60	14582.73
Fiscal Year Total	163532.33	4242.99	21676.23	4107.90	278.35	193837.80

Expenses

	Salaries & Wages	Materials	Rent	Services	Travel & Transp.	Other	Monthly Total
1965							
Sept	2132.78	5554.31	250	1666.66	440.10	164.38	10208.23
Oct	2639.28	9895.16	300	385.60	1040.68	312.52	14573.24
Nov	3260.29	10993.74	250	385.22	534.34	584.87	16008.46
Dec	2828.67	12575.86	250	203.00	758.37	980.83	17596.73
1966							
Jan	3551.95	9774.32	330	455.99	303.50	1136.82	15552.58
Feb	3398.29	7777.44	330	153.35	707.28	309.07	12675.43
Mar	4226.04	11166.11	980	536.95	374.33	949.38	18232.81
Apr	5363.63	8298.46	513.33	471.37	78.71	858.41	15583.91
May	4569.26	9683.99	544.24	624.02	752.68	353.30	16527.49
June	4214.01	5493.32	555	901.20	689.10	313.19	12165.82
July	3433.66	9721.34	580.70	1078.04	447.11	524.66	15785.51
Aug	5406.62	22117.05	691.67	1184.78	416.91	180.90	29997.93
Fiscal Year Total	45024.48	23051.10	5574.94	8046.18	6453.11	6668.33	94908.14

Some adding machines do not hold more than eight figures. If a total exceeds 99,999.99 the next figure at the left pops off and disappears. Because of *(1)* rush in getting figures, *(2)* failure to remember this property of the office adding machine and (3) failure of Mrs. Schwarz to inspect the results, the two compensating errors occurred.

The correct total of expenses is $194,908.14. Operations for the fiscal year resulted in a cash deficit of about $1500. This net is far more believable.

The Habit of Estimating

The evidence about errors in this chapter, combined with our common everyday experience with errors, I think, demonstrate two statements:

- The habit of estimating the range in which a figure should lie is really valuable.
- Estimating ahead of time what a figure should be, and then comparing the estimate with the figure when it becomes known, can be interesting and exciting.

We have mentioned a number of general principles and searching questions for catching errors and being right. Are there any more principles that we can suggest? There are at least these:

- Estimating a figure may be enough to catch an error.
- For catching errors, it is helpful to know a number of scales on which to locate figures reasonably: distances, times, speeds, weights, values, incomes, prices, populations, dates, etc.
- Figures calculated in a rush are "very hot"; they should be allowed to "cool off" for a while, before being used—so that we will have a reasonable time to think about the figures and catch mistakes.
- Every figure should be taken with some grains of salt until confirmed by an independent estimate.
- A great many problems do not have accurate answers, but do have approximate answers, from which sensible decisions can be made.

The cultivated habit of applying the principles of estimating in order to be *right*, and not wrong, can become a keystone to success in many fields.

Part Three

A DOZEN POWERFUL IDEAS MADE EASY TO UNDERSTAND

Mathematics: Variables

WE SHALL NOW BEGIN with the explanation of a dozen
very powerful ideas of mathematics. One of the most powerful and indispensable of all these ideas is the idea of a
variable.

This is the idea of using a letter such as *a* or *b* or *x* (or
some other brief symbol or agreed short name) to stand for
any number (or other mathematical entity, such as a point,
a line, a pattern, etc.) of a certain kind that we may wish to
talk about. When we use such a letter, we imply that we
know the class or group or kind of thing it stands for.

Pronouns in Language

The idea of a variable to stand for a number resembles
very closely the idea of using pronouns — he, him, she, her,
it, they, one, another, etc. — to stand for the names of persons
or things in ordinary language.

By means of this short cut, the variable, we are helped to
express easily many general rules and relations, which if we
adhered to ordinary language would be very long-winded
or difficult to express (illustrations of the help that variables
give will soon appear).

The first branch of mathematics which, according to
tradition, is given the privilege of using pronouns or variables freely is not, however, arithmetic — it is algebra. The

123

traditional rules of ordinary arithmetic, it is sad to say, require us to name every number mentioned by its full proper name, such as 83,726 or 9,841.32.

In other words, arithmetic is like a story told under the rule that every person, whenever mentioned in the story, must always be referred to by his own full name, with no abbreviations allowed, and no matter how often he is referred to:

> "John Livingston entered John Livingston's house, opened the door of the hall closet, hung up John Livingston's hat, and walked into the living room where John Livingston's wife, Emily Livingston, and John Livingston's daughter, Mary Livingston, were playing cards, Mary Livingston with Emily Livingston and Emily Livingston with Mary Livingston."

Algebra is like a story told without this restrictive rule. The rules of algebra and other branches of mathematics permit us to refer to numbers by "pronouns."

We can tell any story in a more convenient way with pronouns:

> "John Livingston entered *his* house, opened the door of the hall closet, hung up *his* hat, and walked into the living room, where *his* wife, Emily, and *his* daughter, Mary, were playing cards with *each other*."

The pronouns "his," "each other" of course are a help. To use the abbreviation "Emily" instead of "Emily Livingston" is a help. Both devices are steps in the direction of using variables.

Expressing Statements with Pronouns

Sometimes there are enough pronouns in English to express clearly something that we may want to say about numbers (or other entities), such as a general rule. Using acceptable English we can say, for example:

> "Whatever number you may choose, it plus itself plus itself is equal to three times it."

For example, if we should choose 17, then 17 plus 17 plus 17 is equal to 3 times 17. At the cost of sounding a little queer, we can even say:

"Whatever number may be chosen, it plus itself plus itself plus itself plus itself is equal to five times it."

For example, if we should choose 23, then 23 plus 23 plus 23 plus 23 plus 23 is 5 times 23. If we want to express a still more general rule, we can, by straining the resources of the English language, say:

"Whatever number may be chosen, it plus itself plus itself, and so on, for a certain total number of occurrences all to be added, is equal to that number of occurrences times the first chosen number."

For example, if we should choose 31, then 31 plus 31 plus 31, and so on, for a total of one hundred occurrences, all to be added, is equal to 100 times 31.

Expressing Statements with Variables

If English possessed two pronouns for "it," which we might call "it_1" (we may say this aloud as "it-one") and "it_2" (we may say this aloud as "it-two"), we could say:

"Whatever two numbers you may choose, it_1 being one of them and it_2 being the other, then it_1 plus it_1 plus it_1, and so on for a total of it_2 occurrences all to be added, is equal to it_2 times it_1."

This hybrid way of speaking is almost mathematical language.

When we let go of words like "it_1" and "it_2," and instead use letters or other compact symbols for numbers, then we have standard mathematical language:

"Whatever two numbers you may choose—let's call them k and n, then k plus k plus k and so on for n occurrences of k to be added is equal to n times k."

This final step of symbolizing seems a simple step to take. Yet it is a step of a most profound and useful kind. This step is usually taken at the start of the subject of algebra. But actually all parts of mathematics, except traditional arithmetic, demand this step, the use of a short compact symbol standing for any mathematical entity of a specified kind—a *variable*.

Algebra naturally retains some of the signs used in arithmetic to stand for operations, such as + for "plus" and × for "times." So the statement becomes:

> "Whatever two numbers may be chosen—let's call them k and n, $k + k + k + \ldots, + k$ for n occurrences of k to be added, equals n times k."

Here k and n are variables. Algebra is a branch of mathematics that talks about numbers and uses variables—letters and other symbols—to stand for numbers.

There are many more instances in language where the linguistic idea of a pronoun (the mathematical idea of a variable) occurs, besides the regular pronouns like "he," "it," "they," "who". . . . Examples are: "the first, the second, the third"; "one, the other"; "the former, the latter"; and even the word "to" in an answering sentence, such as "I would like to."

The Ordinary Mathematical Variable

In mathematics we can usefully distinguish several kinds of variables. We shall discuss three of the kinds.

The first kind of variable is the kind that we have just illustrated, such as k and n as used above. We shall call this the *ordinary mathematical variable*. At the start of a discussion, it stands for whatever number (or other mathematical entity of the kind being discussed) you care to choose; and all during the discussion, wherever the variable is used again, it stands for the same number (or other entity) that you first chose for it. (For example, in a discussion in geometry the variable P may stand for a point and the variable L may stand for a line.)

If you have two ordinary mathematical variables, the

second one may or may not stand for the same number (or other entity) that is chosen for the first variable. For example, in the statement "k plus k plus k and so on for n occurrences of k equals n times k," k and n may or may not stand for the same number, and here both cases may occur. For example, in "4 plus 4 plus 4 plus 4 equals 4 times 4," k and n are the same. In "5 plus 5 plus 5 equals 3 times 5," k and n are different.

The Labeling Variable

The second kind of variable comes in collections of two or more. They are *labels*. They tend to be capital letters. For example, a legal problem may be phrased in this way:

> A steals a car from B, and sells it to C. C, not knowing the car is stolen, sells the car to D. Does the car belong fully to D, who is not only completely innocent, but at least once removed from the theft? If B finds his car in D's possession, can he recover it from D? If so, what is the smallest number of sales to different people that would entitle the resulting owner of the car to keep it?

In this problem, of course, A, B, C, and D all have to be different persons; otherwise the problem would not be sensible.

For another example, let's take this arithmetical puzzle:

> In the following addition of two "disguised" numbers, find out the digits labeled with letters:

$$
\begin{array}{r}
\text{S E N D} \\
+ \ \underline{\text{M O R E}} \\
= \text{M O N E Y}
\end{array}
$$

In this addition, each of the letters stands for a digit, one of 0, 1, 2, 3, 4, 5, 6, 7, 8, 9. Also it is understood and agreed that each different letter stands for a different digit, although in each place where the same letter is used, it stands for the same digit. Thus M stands for a different digit from S. (Can you guess what M stands for? Because of its position in M O N E Y, it is the first digit to be deduced, the first disguise to be seen through.)*

It is often fairly easy to tell, from the context or from a statement explicitly made, that some symbols in a group are together labeling variables, or labels. But it is important to distinguish between labeling variables and ordinary mathematical variables, because the possibility that different letters may perhaps stand for the same number is often important, and the solution of a problem may depend on that possibility.

Any system of nomenclature, any collection of names for distinguishing and identifying a collection of things, is of course a set of labels, a set of labeling variables. One set of names for the collection may of course be quite different from another set. This kind of identifying permeates language. Mathematics, again, is very like ordinary language in recognizing this kind of variable.

For example, all the letters of the alphabet in a language are to be thought of as labeling variables. For instance, when writing English we use the labeling symbol H; we think of it as pronounced "aitch," and associate with it the sound of "h" as in "hand." Yet if we should be dealing with ancient Greek, H is the capital of the letter "eta," written in lower case as η, and the sound it refers to is pronounced like "a" in "pay." The context tells us which meaning to associate with the labeling symbol H.

The Place-Holding Variable

There is a third kind of variable, rather unusual in mathematics, which we shall call the "place-holding variable." This is a symbol which has the property that at its first use in a discussion it stands for any member of the class that you may care to choose, and that at any later use the symbol *still*

* Answer: 9567 plus 1085 equals 10652.

stands for any member of the class that you may care to choose, whether the same as your first choice or different.

This kind of variable is rather like the ordinary use in language of a word with "a" in front of it. If you use the expression "a car" a second time in a discussion, you may or may not be referring to the same car as when you used the expression "a car" the first time. In fact, the chances are good that you are not referring to the same car. If you were, you would probably say "the car" instead.

Though it is common in language, this kind of variable, the place-holding variable, is rather unusual in mathematics. When it does occur in mathematics, it may be represented as an asterisk (*), as in a problem like this:

In the addition of two five-digit numbers (where A and B are different digits):

$$
\begin{aligned}
& * * * A * \\
+ \; & * * * B * \\
\hline
= \; & * * * A *
\end{aligned}
$$

prove that the digit B has to be either 0 or 9.

Here the asterisk denotes any digit at all, and very likely a different digit each time it is used. You could even say that it is marking places or blanks where digits could be inserted.

In the statement of a problem in bridge, a place-holding variable may appear:

North's hand held seven Hearts, A Q J 10 x x x.

Here, the symbol x is used "to hold a place for" each of the three remaining cards in North's hand, all of them (by convention in the game of bridge) bearing a number 9 or less. We know from our knowledge of the deck of 52 cards that the three cards cannot bear the same numbers. But the differences between the possible values of x x x from 9, 8, 7 down to 4, 3, 2 is unimportant for the purposes of discussion of the bridge game. And so the symbolism, as usual in any good language, ignores the differences, so that they do not have to receive attention.

But the most important kind of variable is the ordinary

mathematical variable (usually a letter), which, when it first occurs in a discussion, stands for any one of a class of values (usually, numbers), and at any later use in the discussion stands for the same value (usually, number) which was chosen at the first occurrence.

How to Go from Ideas to Letters

How do we choose a letter to stand for a numerical idea expressed in words? More generally, how do we choose a symbol to stand for some mathematical idea that may vary?

There is a regular procedure for doing this:

1) Establish clearly (by definition, counting, measurement, or in some other way) the idea we are interested in. This gives the specification or *definition* of the variable.

2) Establish clearly the class or set or kind or collection (or *range*) of the numbers (or other elements) that the idea may stand for. These are the *values* of the variable.

3) Choose a letter (or a brief symbol) to stand for or represent the defined idea. Often the letter can be the initial letter of a key word in the definition.

For example, if we are talking about a room, and its area, length, and width, then it is natural to choose the initial letters A, L, and W, of the key words area, length, and width. Then A, L, and W will stand for these ideas respectively. If we are talking about a circle, it is natural to choose the letters D for diameter and C for circumference.

When we choose letters that are to be brief symbols for numerical ideas, we must also choose the units in which to count or measure the ideas numerically. If length is measured in miles, then width should be measured in miles, and area in square miles. Some units are conspicuous, as when we count individuals. Other units are established only by convention, as when we adopt the pound as a unit for measuring the weight of an object.

In mathematics the letters usually selected for variables are often small letters of the alphabet, though capital letters are also used. Also a, b, c, and d are generally used for numbers that are supposed to be known at the start of a problem (though they may change from problem to problem), and x, y, and z are often used for numbers that are supposed to be not known at the start of the problem (unknown numbers). After these letters have been assigned to duties, other letters are freely used, such as m, n, p, and u, v, and w. The letters o and O are, however, often avoided because they may be confused with zero.

When this supply of letters for variables for representing numbers being referred to is exhausted, or even sooner, there is a tendency to use subscript numbers: instead of a, b, c, there is a tendency to use a_1 (read "a sub one"), a_2 (read "a sub two"), a_3 (read "a sub three"), etc.; or pairs of subscripts may be used: b_{11}, b_{21}, b_{31} . . . b_{13}, b_{14}, b_{15} . . . (read "b sub one one, b sub two one," etc.) None of these choices of symbols, of course, are to be considered burdensome or difficult in themselves. All of them are simply ways for efficiently naming numbers (or other mathematical entities) that somebody desires to talk about.

How to Go from Letters to Numbers

How do we go from a letter to a number? More generally, how do we go from a variable to a particular value of the variable?

There is a regular procedure for doing this also:
1) Choose some number (or value) that is in the class of numbers (or values) which the letter may stand for.
2) Put the number (or value) into the discussion where the letter is used, making sure that it fits.

For example, if we are talking about the length L of a room, we could choose $8\frac{1}{2}$ feet for the length L, in which case the room would be quite small; or we could choose 25 feet for the length L, in which case the room would be quite large; or we could choose some in-between number, such as 14 feet. Any reasonable choice of a number which we happen to make is likely to be a good value of the variable.

Of course, if several variables occur together in a definite relation, we may not be able to choose freely any value for each one. For example, since the area of a room is equal to the length times the width, we can choose some number for the length L and we can choose some other number for the width W, but then the area A will be determined (since it is the product of L times W), and we can no longer choose freely a number for the value of A.

Properties of the Ordinary Mathematical Variable

To sum up, the most important kind of variable is the ordinary mathematical variable. Here are some true statements about it to be remembered:

1) In a discussion, the ordinary mathematical variable is a letter (or other symbol) that may stand for any one of a specified (or understood) class of numbers (or other mathematical entities).

2) At its first use in the discussion, it stands for any one of that class that you may care to choose and that meets the conditions of the problem. What it stands for is its *value*.

3) At each later use in the discussion, it stands for the same value that you chose the first time.

4) The symbol for a variable is often, but not always, a letter.

5) The class of values is often, but not always, a class of numbers.

Other kinds of symbols that vary in what they stand for also appear in mathematics. But the ordinary mathematical variable is the most useful of the several kinds of variables, and is a crucially important and powerful mathematical idea.

Formulas

10

The Idea: Rules in Language, Formulas in Mathematics

As soon as we are able to use variables, we can express formulas. What is a formula? A *formula* is a brief statement using symbols that expresses a general rule. The idea of the formula is one of the most important and powerful of all the ideas in mathematics.

Let us look over some examples where rules and formulas arise.

A Rule About the Area of a Room

What is the area of an ordinary room? An "ordinary" room is one with four straight sides at right angles to each other. An "extraordinary" room is not like this—it may have irregular walls, or more than four sides, or the walls may not be at right angles to each other.

There are several ways of expressing the rule that will tell us the area of an ordinary room. They range from expressing all the information in ordinary language to expressing all the information in mathematical symbols.

1) To find the area of a room in square feet, multiply the length of the room in feet by the width of the room in feet.

133

This version of the rule is expressed in ordinary, acceptable English language.

    2) The area of a room in square feet is equal to the product of its length in feet and its width in feet.

Here the rule is still expressed in ordinary, acceptable English language.

    3) (The area of the room in square feet) EQUALS
       (the length of the room in feet) TIMES
       (the width of the room in feet).

Here the rule is expressed partly in ordinary language and partly in mathematical language. The mathematical language consists of two parts: first, mathematical parentheses, which mark the boundaries of each idea; and second, mathematical words—EQUALS and TIMES—standing for mathematical operations. Mathematical parentheses, here illustrated, are a remarkably useful device; to do the same job in ordinary language, we have to get along with an unsystematic use of punctuation such as commas and words such as "which," to mark the boundaries of ideas.

    4) Let A equal the area of the room in square feet; let L equal its length in feet; and let W equal its width in feet. Then A equals L times W.

Here the rule is expressed essentially in mathematical language using variables; but ordinary words are also used.

    5) $A = L \times W$

Here we have a formula expressed in mathematics. When using it, we must, of course, remember how much meaning has been packed into the definitions of A, L, and W.

    For example, if the room were $18\frac{1}{2}$ feet long and ten feet wide, then the area of the room would be $18\frac{1}{2}$ times 10 (in square feet)—equal to 185 square feet.

A Rule About the Difference of Two Squares

Let us now look at another more complicated rule expressed in language; and let us trace, slowly and deliberately, the successive stages of turning it into a formula.

VERSION 1

> The difference resulting from a number multiplied by itself less another number multiplied by itself, is always equal to the product of the sum of the first number and the second number, times the difference resulting from subtracting the second number from the first number.

What in the world does this mean?

To make sure of the meaning, let us first write this rule in the style of a cookbook recipe or an income tax form, as a series of steps to be taken one after another. The result of each step gives an item.

VERSION 2

(1) Choose one number; this is Item (1).

(2) Choose a second number; this is Item (2).

(3) Multiply the first number, Item (1), by itself, and call this result Item (3).

(4) Multiply the second number, Item (2), by itself, and call this result Item (4).

(5) Subtract Item (4) from Item (3), and call the result Item (5).

(6) Add the first number, Item (1), and the second number, Item (2), and call the result Item (6).

(7) Subtract Item (2) from Item (1), and call the result Item (7).

(8) Multiply Item (6) by Item (7), and call the result Item (8).

(9) If the rule is correct, then Item (5) will always equal Item (8).

This reminds us very much of the way in which the entries in an income tax form are calculated.

Suppose we check the rule to see if it is true, choosing, say, for the first number, 10 and for the second number, 2:

> *Example*
> (1) Choose 10.
> (2) Choose 2.
> (3) 10 times 10 is 100.
> (4) 2 times 2 is 4.
> (5) Subtract Item (4) from Item (3): 100 minus 4 is 96; this is Item (5).
> (6) 10 plus 2 is 12.
> (7) 10 minus 2 is 8.
> (8) Multiply Item (6) by Item (7): 12 times 8 is 96; this is Item (8).
> (9) In this case, Item (5), which is 96, equals Item (8), which is 96.

The two results agree; so the rule in the case of these two numbers is neatly verified. The rule asserts that this result happens in all cases; but of course one example does not prove the assertion; the proof is given in Appendix 1.

Now let us write this rule in language that is a little more like mathematics, using the following important method:

> *Method for Clarifying Meaning*
> *1)* Notice each idea being stated, and put a pair of parentheses around the words referring to it (these are mathematical parentheses).
> *2)* Notice each relation being stated or asserted, and write in capitals all the words referring to it.

This is a useful and general method for making clearer the meaning of something. But other ways of marking ideas and relations may, of course, be just as good. For example, we could use red pencil for underlining the ideas, and blue pencil for underlining the relations and assertions.

Using the first method, we obtain Version 3.

VERSION 3

THE DIFFERENCE RESULTING FROM (a number) MULTIPLIED BY (itself) LESS (another number) MULTIPLIED BY (itself) IS ALWAYS EQUAL TO THE PRODUCT OF THE SUM OF (the first number) AND (the second number), TIMES THE DIFFERENCE RESULTING FROM SUBTRACTING (the second number) FROM (the first number).

We can rephrase this version, simplifying the wording a little, and obtain Version 4:

VERSION 4

(A first number) TIMES (the first number), LESS (a second number) TIMES (the second number), ALWAYS EQUALS THE PRODUCT OF THE SUM OF (the first number) AND (the second number), AND THE DIFFERENCE OF (the first number) LESS (the second number).

Now we are ready to take the crucial step, going from words and phrases denoting ideas to variables (letters or other symbols) denoting ideas:

Let a stand for the first number that may be chosen.

Let b stand for the second number that may be chosen.

Now the rule may be rephrased quite simply:

VERSION 5

a TIMES a, LESS b TIMES b, ALWAYS EQUALS THE PRODUCT OF a PLUS b, AND a MINUS b.

Now we can use the familiar signs of arithmetic, $+$ for PLUS, $-$ for MINUS, $\times$ for TIMES, and $=$ for EQUALS, replacing words. We obtain:

VERSION 6

$$a \times a - b \times b, = a + b, \times a - b$$

But we have not yet said clearly what we mean, because the leftover commas are not enough to tell us precisely which one of several possible meanings is intended, depending on the way in which we group the operations. What shall we do?

We have to use an additional layer of mathematical parentheses since they show how ideas are to be grouped or associated with each other. We do this work in ordinary language with words. For example take the words:

THE PRODUCT OF THE SUM OF . . . AND . . . , AND
THE DIFFERENCE OF . . . LESS . . .

This tells us: first, we have to find a sum and a difference; then, and only then, do we multiply the sum and the difference together, and get a product.

Using mathematical parentheses for grouping, we write:

VERSION 7

$$(a \times a) - (b \times b) = (a + b) \times (a - b)$$

This tells us, without allowing more than one meaning, which operations have to be done first: namely, those in parentheses.

In this series of steps one after another to reach a neat formula, there is one more step that we can take. This is to make use of a^2 (read "a squared") to stand for $a \times a$ (and similarly for any other variable). So we can write:

VERSION 8

$$a^2 - b^2 = (a + b) \times (a - b)$$

This final style is a good example of a neat and compact formula. Just as the notation of Arabic numerals makes arithmetical calculation much easier, so this kind of neat and compact notation for formulas makes calculating, proving, and problem-solving much easier than it would be otherwise.

Using the short style, we can easily write down some more examples. They are shown in the table below.

Examples of $(a^2 - b^2) = (a + b) \times (a - b)$

If a is:	and if b is:	then a^2 minus b^2 is:	and $a + b$ times $a - b$ is:
10	1	100 minus 1, which is 99	11 times 9, which is 99
10	3	100 minus 9, which is 91	13 times 7, which is 91
10	4	100 minus 16, which is 84	14 times 6, which is 84
20	1	400 minus 1, which is 399	21 times 19, which is 399
20	2	400 minus 4, which is 396	22 times 18, which is 396

And of course, we still have not proved the rule, but just illustrated it.

How to Go from a Rule to a Formula

This example—the rule about the difference of two squares—has been dissected like a frog's leg in a biology class—it has been taken apart in fine detail to show just what each step is—and just when each step is taken. With this example in front of us as a model, we can write down a general procedure for going from a rule expressed in words to a formula expressed in mathematics:

1) Notice each numerical idea (or other mathematical entity) referred to.
2) Mark each such idea with a letter, using the same letter when the same idea occurs again.
3) Notice the relations and assertions being stated.
4) Translate them into the signs of arithmetic (and other signs of mathematics).
5) Notice the sequence of the steps in the program of operations.
6) Express this sequence of steps with mathematical parentheses to show grouping.

To make this procedure as clear as possible, the previous example should be examined again, and the steps in it compared with the steps described in general here.

A Rule About Vacations

Let us now consider some more examples of rules, and how they may be translated into formulas.

Here is a rule about vacations of new employees of a company, expressed in words.

VERSION 1

Each employee, if he becomes employed after July 1 in the previous year and before July 1 in the current year, will be entitled to a first vacation, such that the number of his days of vacation not including Sundays will be equal to the number of his full months of employment from the date of his employment up to the July 1 in the current year.

For instance, suppose we have the case of a man who began to be employed on August 15, 1965, who desires to take a vacation beginning October 22, 1966, and who has had an interruption of employment from December 1, 1965 to January 15, 1966. This man has had $3\frac{1}{2}$ months of employment from August 15 to December 1, and $5\frac{1}{2}$ months of employment from January 15 to July 1, and so he has had a total of nine months of employment. Therefore, he will be entitled to nine days of vacation not including Sundays, and so, on October 22, 1966, although he has now worked $3\frac{1}{2}$ months more from July 1, 1966, his vacation will run from October 22 to November 1, inclusive (October 23 and 30 being Sundays).

What will this rule be like when expressed as a formula?

VERSION 2

Let m equal the number of completed months of employment of an employee who becomes employed in the period after July 1 in the previous year and before July 1 in the current year.

Let v equal the number of days of vacation, not
including Sundays, to which the employee is entitled in his first vacation.
Then v equals m: $v = m$.

The formula $v = m$ is a good illustration of how short a
formula can become, although of course a great deal of meaning has been packed into the definitions of m and v.

A Rule About Distance, Time, and Speed

Here is a rule about distance traveled, the time spent,
and the average speed. This rule is familiar to all of us:
The time spent by a moving object multiplied by its
average speed is equal to the distance traveled.
Separating the ideas from the relations:
(The time spent by a moving object) MULTIPLIED BY
(its average speed) IS EQUAL TO (the distance traveled).
Suppose we let t be the time spent (say, in hours), and
let s be the average speed (say, in miles per hour), and let d
be the distance traveled (say, in miles). Then we have:
t TIMES s EQUALS d
Using the signs of arithmetic:
$t \times s = d$

A Rule for Reconciling Your Checkbook Balance
and the Bank Balance

If you have a checking account with a bank, the bank
regularly sends you at the end of the month a statement
showing how much money the bank says you have in the
bank. You may be the kind of person who keeps a careful
record of your checks and deposits — and you may even
record a balance in your checkbook after each transaction.
When the bank statement comes, there is a difference between what you record that you have and what the bank

states that you have. And the big question is, Is the difference serious? Has anybody make a mistake?

The main reason, of course, for any difference is that you
and the bank do have different knowledge of the transactions
that have happened. Each of you knows about some transactions which the other of you does not know about; for example, if you have deposited a check in Canadian money,
the bank computes and subtracts a discount which you don't
know precisely until the bank statement comes.

For reconciling your record and the bank's record, here
is the procedure:

When you receive the bank statement at the end of the
month, you check off or tally in your checkbook all checks
that the bank has recorded; you also tally in your checkbook
all deposits that the bank has recorded. Then you choose a
convenient date, such as the 29th day of the month (this is
the day closest to the bank's knowledge of your account, and
should lead to the least amount of work), and you apply the
following rule for reconciling:

· (your Balance shown in the Bank statement)

MINUS (all Earlier Untallied Checks — because the bank
did not know that you no longer had that money)

PLUS (all Earlier Untallied Deposits — because the bank
did not know at statement time that you had sent them
those deposits)

PLUS (all Later Tallied Checks and Charges — because
your checkbook balance on the 29th day of the month
did not include them)

MINUS (all Later Tallied Deposits — because your checkbook balance on the 29th day of the month did not
include them either — for example, a deposit you for-
got that the bank did not forget)

MINUS (what your Checkbook shows as your Balance on
the 29th day of the month)

EQUALS ("Heaven Knows What," the real difference)

In this case, it is convenient to choose sets of letters (as names or variables) to stand for the seven numerical ideas that appear in the rule. (The letters chosen are in capital letters in the phrases above.) So the reconciling rule expressed as a formula becomes:

$$BB - EUC + EUD + LTC - LTD - CB = HKW$$

If the *HKW* is zero, hurray!—you and the bank agree.

If the *HKW* is small and positive, the bank thinks you have a little more than you think you have, and you might just as well add the *HKW* into your checkbook balance, tally it for the next month, and let good things alone! This saves a great deal of time.

If the *HKW* is small and negative, the bank thinks you have less than you think you have, and it might just be sensible to accept the bank's dimmer view, subtract the *HKW* from your checkbook balance, and tally it now for next month's reconciling, looking on it as a charge for wear and tear.

If the *HKW* is big, you have a problem—you have to hunt and hunt for the reason until you find out why. And for most people, this is an unpleasant chore. For example, once when I had two accounts (business and personal) in the same bank, a large deposit through their error went into the wrong account, and it took me several hours to discover and identify the error.

The Pythagorean Formula

Many formulas either do not have names or else are named "the formula for" some purpose, like the formula for the area of a room. But some formulas have played such an important part in the history of ideas that they have acquired names. One of these formulas is the Pythagorean Formula, which was named after an ancient Greek philosopher and mathematician, Pythagoras.

This formula is expressed in the rule (or theorem):

For every right triangle [that is, a triangle which has one of its angles a right angle] the sum of the squares on the two shorter sides [these are the sides next to the right angle] is equal to the square on the hypotenuse [the longest side].

In the subject of plane geometry as taught in high school, this is one of the theorems that most students learn to prove. The student "constructs" three squares on the three sides of an "arbitrary" right triangle (one which is not "special" in any way). Then, after drawing certain additional "construction" lines, the student proves that the area of the largest square is equal to the sum of the areas of the two smaller squares.

Some right triangles have side lengths which can all be expressed in whole numbers of units. One famous right triangle, with sides 3 units, 4 units, and 5 units, has for more than 4,000 years been used by carpenters (from Egypt onward) to determine right angles:

$$(3 \times 3) + (4 \times 4) = (5 \times 5)$$
$$9 \quad + \quad 16 \quad = \quad 25$$

To express this rule as a formula, we would say:

Let a and b be the two shorter sides of a right triangle; let h be the hypotenuse. Then, for every right triangle:

$$a^2 + b^2 = h^2$$

It is an interesting fact that flatness and the Pythagorean Formula are related. If the Pythagorean Formula is true for every right triangle that can be drawn in a surface, then the surface is flat (nowhere curved). If a surface is flat, then for every right triangle that can be drawn in it, the Pythagorean Formula is true. For this reason, an astronomer who wonders if space is curved and not flat may search for a right-angled triangle among the stars for which the Pythagorean Formula is not true.

And of course we could give many, many more examples of formulas.

The Role of Formulas in Mathematics

Much of mathematics is made up of formulas. Very few of the formulas are difficult in themselves. Often, though, a great deal of meaning has been packed into the definitions of the symbols which appear in the formulas, and to grasp all that meaning takes hard work.

Certainly the idea of a formula, the idea of a compact rule summarizing a large amount of true information, and made compact by using specially defined symbols, is a mathematical idea of the utmost power.

Functions and Graphs

ANOTHER OF the thousand-horsepower ideas of mathematics is the idea of a *function*. Before we try to make clear
the mathematical meaning of this idea, let us look among the
expressions of common everyday language and see what we
find there analogous to this idea. For, as we have said often
and will say many times more, quantities of the important
ideas of mathematics can be found in elementary and very
familiar form in ordinary language.

The Idea: Dependence in Language, Function in Mathematics

When something *depends on* something else, as we say
in common everyday talk, then that something *is a function
of* the something else, to use the language of mathematics.
For example:

"Father, can we go picnicking tomorrow, Sunday?"
"I don't know, sonny—it depends."
"What does it depend on, Father?"
"Well, if the weather is warm and sunny, and if your
sister Janie is over her cold, and if I can finish the
planting in the garden that I have to do tomorrow
morning, then we can go picnicking."

146

Using mathematical language:
(Going picnicking tomorrow) IS A FUNCTION OF (the weather, sister Janie's health, AND father's success in planting tomorrow morning).

Here is another example:
The temperature yesterday was in the low 60's in the morning, in the low 80's in the afternoon, and about 73 last night.
Using mathematical language:
(The temperature yesterday) WAS A FUNCTION OF (the time of day yesterday).

Here is another example:
"How long will it take me to drive to New York?"
"Well, it depends on what road you take, how fast you travel, and the traffic conditions."
Using mathematical language:
(The time it will take me to get to New York) IS A FUNCTION OF (the road I take, how fast I travel, AND the traffic conditions).

Whenever something Y (a decision, a condition, a magnitude, a thing, a person, etc.) *depends on* one or more other factors or elements X (decisions, conditions, magnitudes, things, persons, etc.), then Y is said to be *a function of* X. In other words, Y is said to be a function of X if when X is given, Y is determined. Notice that here the symbol X may stand for just one factor or element or may stand for two or more; the symbol X, in other words, may be interpreted as singular or plural. The word "determined" means "settled," "fixed," "found out," "established"; the "determining" may involve a connection of cause and effect, or may refer to some very different kind of association or correlation where no cause and effect are involved at all.

Examples of Functions

Let us consider some examples where X and Y are both persons. Here are some functions:

the father of . . .
the eldest son of . . . and - - -
the paternal grandfather of . . .
the last doctor who treated . . .
the first ancestor of . . . who came to America
the best teacher of . . .

Here are some examples where X and Y are both statements:

the denial of . . .
the statement that both . . . and - - - are true

Here are some examples of functions where X and Y are both stations on a railroad:

the last station preceding . . .
the next station following . . .
the first junction following . . .

Here are some examples of functions where X and Y are both numbers:

the square of . . .
the result of multiplying . . . by itself
43 times . . .
the nearest round number to . . .
the sum of . . . , - - - , $*\ *\ *$, and _____

In view of all these examples—and a great many more could be very easily offered—you and I can probably agree at this point that functions are very common, and permeate all ordinary language and discussion. In fact, very often, whenever we can say sensibly:

the . . . of

we are making use of a function.

A function, in other words, is a relation (or specification or rule or statement or formula) expressed in such a way that if one or more variables are given, another variable is determined.

There are differences between a formula and a function. If we take, for example, the formula:

(the Area of a room) EQUALS (its Length) TIMES (its Width), $A = L \times W$

then we can specify three functions:

- the area, which depends on the length and the width, $A = L \times W$
- the length, which depends on the area and the width, $L = A \div W$
- the width, which depends on the area and the length, $W = A \div L$

We can also say that:

The formula for Y in terms of X states the relation Y as a function of X.

If we are talking about a function in general, it may be designated by F, or G, or H, or f, or g, or by similar letters. We have here a variable standing for any function. These letters are useful for talking about any functions, in the same way as other letters like x, y, or z, are useful for talking about any numbers.

To say briefly that Y is a function of X, we often write $Y = f(X)$, read "Y equals f of X."

We can now illustrate some relations between functions. For example: (the mother of the father of . . .) IS THE SAME AS (the paternal grandmother of . . .).

This is an illustration of what is called the *functional product* "F of G of . . ." In this case, "F of G of . . ." equals "H of . . ." where F is the mother of, G is the father of, and H is the paternal grandmother of.

Ideas Related to the Idea of a Function: Independence, Dependence, Values, Ranges

We have said enough now, perhaps, so that we can talk

about some of the ideas closely connected with the idea of a function.

Two of these ideas are the *independent* variable (or variables), and the *dependent variable*. If Y is a function of X, then Y is called the *dependent* variable, because Y depends on X, and X is called the independent variable (or variables), because it is (they are) free to vary in the situation that is being discussed. Any particular instances of X or Y are called *values*.

For example, suppose we consider the area of a room as a function (namely, the product) of the length and the width. Suppose also in some case the length is $18\frac{1}{2}$ feet and the width is ten feet. Then we can say:

- the value of the length (in feet) is $18\frac{1}{2}$;
- the value of the width (in feet) is 10; and
- the corresponding value of the area (in square feet) is 185.

For another example, suppose we consider the function "the successor of" and allow its values to be Presidents of the United States. Then we have the following instances (among others):

- H. S Truman was the successor of F. D. Roosevelt;
- D. D. Eisenhower was the successor of Truman;
- J. F. Kennedy was the successor of Eisenhower.

In the case of the function "Y is the successor of X," Eisenhower is a value of both X and Y, and so is Truman. George Washington, however, is not the successor of any other President, and so George Washington is a value of X but not a value of Y.

The entire collection of values of X is called the *range* (or *domain*) of X. The entire collection of values of Y is called the *range* of Y. And we may speak of either variable as *varying over* its range. In the just-given example, the range of X and Y considered together is the class of Presidents of the United States.

Tables — Summaries of Functions

The specification of how each value of X is matched up with its corresponding value of Y is the complete specification of the function. This specification can often be expressed very well in a table, especially where the extent of the function is small. For example, the three statements above can be summarized in a table as follows:

If **X** is:	Then **Y**, the Successor of **X**, is:
F. D. Roosevelt	H. S Truman
H. S Truman	D. D. Eisenhower
D. D. Eisenhower	J. F. Kennedy

In this case the entire table expressing this function for all the instances (values) that have occurred up to 1965 would take less than forty lines (or entries).

To consider another situation, let's take four directions, North, East, South, and West, and the function "the opposite direction from." The following table expresses this function:

If **X** is:	Then **Y**, the Opposite Direction from **X**, is:
North	South
East	West
South	North
West	East

In this table only four lines are needed to tell the whole story.

A very familiar table is the ordinary multiplication table in the scale of 10. Here is a little part of it:

	... 6	7	8 ...
3	18	21	24
4	24	28	32
5	30	35	40

When written in full, the multiplication table shows down the side labeling the horizontal rows any whole number from 0 to 9 (let's call it X). It also shows along the top labeling the columns any whole number from 0 to 9 (let's call it W). Inside the table where each row and column intersect is a cell, and in the cell we put the product of X times W, the result of multiplying the number X labeling the row and the number W labeling the column. Let us call the contents of the cell the number Y. Y is a function of the variables X and W — it is *the product of* X *and* W. For example, if X has the value 4, and W has the value 7, then the function Y has the value 28. This situation, of course, is very simple and elementary, except that we are using new language — the language of the mathematical words "function, variable, value," etc. — to talk about the situation.

A list can be thought of as a table of two columns. The first column is not explicitly written but is implied; it contains the numbers 1, 2, 3 . . . identifying the rows of the list. The second column contains the entries of the list.

Can every function be expressed by a table? In theory, yes: a function is a table, and a table is a function. But in practice many tables would be far too big for human beings to deal with in their entirety. And so other ways of specifying functions need to be used also.

How to Make a Table

Is there a general procedure for making a table? Yes, and here it is:

1) Choose some values of X. Let us call them $X_1, X_2, X_3 \ldots$
2) Using the rule specifying the function, calculate (determine) the corresponding values of Y, calling them $Y_1, Y_2, Y_3 \ldots$
3) Arrange them in a list, with the successive values of X in the left-hand column and the successive values of Y in the right-hand column.

4) Choose precise descriptions for each column of the table.

But, you may say, how about Step 1? How should I choose the values of X? It depends! The choice is a function of what you know, what you can find out, your experience, the context or situation, etc. Sometimes it takes a great deal of study to choose wisely the values of X to go into a table. But most of the time the context or situation tells us plainly what choice to make — because we want to cut down the work of saying almost the same thing in a large number of separate sentences:

Two times two is four.

Three times three is nine.

Four times four is 16.

. . .

Nine times nine is 81.

Ten times ten is one hundred.

. . .

25 times 25 is 625.

. . .

We express the common framework of the sentences in the framework of the table, and then just fill in the columns:

If the number **X** is:	Then the number times itself, **Y**, is:
2	4
3	9
4	16
5	25
. . .	. . .
9	81
10	100
. . .	. . .
25	625
. . .	. . .

The Classification of Functions

There are some broad classes of functions. A *single-valued function* is one that always has a single value. For example, "father of" is a single-valued function, because every person has one and only one father. A *many-valued function* is a function that often has more than one value. For example, "friend of" is a many-valued function because a person often has more than one friend. Nearly all the time in mathematics we deal with single-valued functions, because we can calculate usefully with them.

Functions may also be classified according to the number of their independent variables. A function may be a *function of one variable:* it has just one independent variable. For example, "the next following station to . . ." is a function of just one variable; "the next following station to" two or more stations would have no sensible meaning. Or a function may be a *function of two variables.* For example, "the difference between" is a function of two variables: "The difference between 7 and 19 is 12." Or a function may be a *function of an indefinite number of variables:* "the sum of" is such a function. The sum of the first 31 numbers 1, 2, 3, . . . 31 is 496; the sum of 22 and 33 is 55; and we can, if we choose, define "the sum of 13" as being just 13.

In our discussion on page 153, we allowed X to refer to one or more variables, without distinguishing between the cases. To be more precise, however, if X does refer to two or more variables, then we usually write each variable separately (using a different letter or symbol for each variable).

For example:
   * * * is the sum of . . . and - - - and _____
would become:
   Y is the sum of X and W and U
or else:
   Y is the sum of X_1 and X_2 and X_3

The subscripts $_1$, $_2$, $_3$, etc. (as in X_1, X_2, X_3), are usually very convenient to identify the first one of some kind, the second one of the same kind, the third one of the same kind, and so on.

Continuous Functions

For some functions, the possible values of X and Y are entities that have wide separations between them. This is true for "the father of"; if Y is the father of X, we know that all the values of X and Y are separate distinct persons who do not merge into each other. This kind of variable and this kind of function are called *discontinuous*.

But for some other functions the possible values of the variable X (though still separate and distinct) are closely connected, and, in fact, they appear to merge into each other. For example, if X is distance, or time, or electrical voltage, or force, etc., in the real world we seem always to be able to find a value of X in between two previous values of X. For example, if one value of X is ten feet, and another value of X is $10\frac{1}{2}$ feet, we can, in fact, observe an in-between value of $10\frac{1}{4}$ feet. Also, we believe or we assume that we could, if we wished to and had suitable instruments, observe a distance equal to ten feet plus, say, one millionth of a foot, or even a smaller fraction.

In these cases we call X a *continuous variable*, meaning a smoothly changing variable. The same can be true of Y, the function of X.

Suppose we consider the function:

> Y is the temperature of a certain day at a certain place at time T.

Then if we have two times very close together, our experience with temperatures tells us that the temperatures will be very close together. In other words, if we take an in-between value of the time, we will find that the corresponding value of the temperature is very close.

For example, suppose we observe a temperature of 56.0 degrees at time 9:00 A.M. on a certain day at a certain place. Suppose we also observe a temperature of 56.1 degrees at 9:05 A.M. on the same day at the same place. Then, from our experience of time and temperature, we know that at 9:04 A.M. the temperature will be very close to both these temperatures. At 9:04 A.M. the temperature might be 56.2 or 56.0 degrees. More likely, it would be 56.1 degrees. It would not be 88.7 degrees, because Nature does not make violent jumps like this in temperature (though Nature might make violent jumps in some other variable).

If Y is a function of X, and both X and Y are *continuous variables*, then the function is called a *continuous function*.

Mathematicians have arrived at a very precise definition of a continuous function, and it would be possible to state this definition here. But the definition is not at all easy to grasp when first met; so, for our purposes here, we simply use the common everyday idea of "continuous," meaning closely connected and smoothly changing without sudden or violent jumps. This use of the common everyday idea of continuity is reasonable, because this idea was used for centuries before mathematicians finally obtained their precise and rigorous mathematical definition in the 1800's.

How to Use a Table for In-Between Cases

When we have evidence that a function changes smoothly (is continuous), we can use a small table to give a very large amount of information.

For example, suppose we have a table of six lines showing heights and weights, such as the table on facing page. (This table gives the average weight of American men ages 30 to 39 corresponding to their height. The weight is taken in ordinary indoor clothing; the height is measured with shoes; and the study producing these figures was made by the Society of Actuaries in 1959. The table is taken from information shown in the *1966 World Almanac*, page 303.)

Height (in feet and inches)		Weight (in pounds)
5	0	131
5	3	141
5	6	153
5	9	165
6	0	179
6	3	193

Only six cases are shown in this table. Of course, all possible heights are very numerous. In fact, if we measured the heights of men to the nearest quarter of an inch, we would obtain 85 possible heights in the range, say, from 4 feet 9 inches to 6 feet 6 inches inclusive, for which this table could readily give information.

However, although this table has only six items of information, it is easy to use the information given to determine quite closely what would be the average weight of a man for any height in this range.

Suppose, for example, we had a man whose height was 5 feet 7 inches. His case is not in the table. For 5 feet 6 inches, shown in the table, the weight given is 153 pounds. For 5 feet 9 inches the weight shown is 165 pounds.

Now 5 feet 7 inches is one third of the way along from 5 feet 6 inches to 5 feet 9 inches (the nearest cases in the table). Therefore, using the experience we have had with smoothly changing functions, we would expect that the average weight for this man's height would be very close to one third of the way along from 153 pounds to 165 pounds, a difference of 12 pounds. Now 1/3 of 12 pounds is 4 pounds. So adding the 4 pounds to the 153 pounds, we would estimate the average weight for this man's height as 157 pounds.

The method we have just used is a general and powerful method, useful in a great many situations. It has a name — *linear interpolation*. There are other kinds of interpolation which may be more accurate in some situations; for these methods adjectives different from "linear" are used. We can express the method of linear interpolation in a procedure or recipe:

1) Find the place in the table where X would fall.
2) Find X_1, which is the nearest X-value in the table smaller than X.
3) Find X_2, which is the nearest X-value in the table larger than X.
4) Calculate the fraction: (X minus X_1) divided by (X_2 minus X_1).
5) Find the difference between Y_2 and Y_1.
6) Multiply the difference, Item 5, by the fraction, Item 4.
7) Add Item 6 to Y_1, and take this as the estimate of the value of Y corresponding to the value of X.

We can also express this method as a formula:

$$Y = Y_1 + \frac{(X - X_1)}{(X_2 - X_1)} \times (Y_2 - Y_1)$$

But in order to be justified in using this method, we must have information that the variables X and Y are changing smoothly, rather than jumping all over the lot. In the case of the average weight of American men as a function of their height, we do know that both variables are changing smoothly.

Graphs—How a Function Can Be Pictured

Let us now consider a particular example of the kind of function we have called closely connected (continuous). Figure 1 shows two scales, one called an X scale and another

X	-40	-20	0	20	40	60	80	100	120	140
Y	-40	-4	32	68	104	140	176	212	248	284

Figure 1. Two scales matched up with each other.

called a *Y* scale, matched up with each other. For example, 20 on the *X* scale is matched with 68 on the *Y* scale; and 40 on the *X* scale is matched with 104 on the *Y* scale. We look over the numbers written on each scale; we notice that every interval on the *X* scale is 20 units, and that every interval on the *Y* scale is 36 units. We feel sure that for any number on the *X* scale we can find exactly one corresponding number on the *Y* scale.

Someone looking over our shoulder tells us:

"Any number *Y* on the lower scale can be found to be equal to nine-fifths of the number *X* on the upper scale, plus 32."

We say, "How do you know?" He laughs and does not reply.

Let's see if this rule is actually true. For example, 20 on the *X* scale is matched with 68 on the *Y* scale; 9/5 of 20 is 36; add 32; and the result is 68. This verifies.

For another example, 40 on the *X* scale is matched with 104 on the *Y* scale; 9/5 of 40 is 72; add 32; the result is 104. This also verifies. It looks as if the rule is true.

By more calculation, we can determine that the rule is verified for all ten pairs of numbers shown on the scales. We can translate the rule into the language of mathematics. The successive stages of translation are as follows:

1) Any number on the lower scale is equal to nine fifths of the corresponding number on the upper scale plus thirty-two.

2) (the number on the lower scale, *Y*) EQUALS (nine-fifths) OF (the corresponding number on the upper scale, *X*) PLUS (thirty-two).

3) *Y* equals 9/5 of *X* plus 32.

4) $Y = 9/5\ X + 32$

The only picture we have of our function so far is the picture of the two scales drawn right next to each other. But suppose that we now make several changes. First we turn the *Y* scale around at right angles, with the smallest value at

the bottom. Second, we draw copies of it, as often as necessary, as a vertical straight line right next to each X value on
the X scale. Third, we position these Y scales so that the zero
mark of each one is located on the line of the X scale. Fourth,
we adopt the same units of measurement for the Y scale as
we did for the X scale. And finally, for each value of X, we
mark with a dot on its vertical Y scale the value of Y which
corresponds.

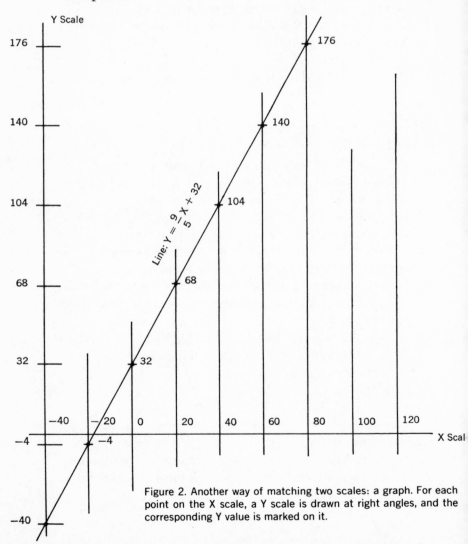

Figure 2. Another way of matching two scales: a graph. For each
point on the X scale, a Y scale is drawn at right angles, and the
corresponding Y value is marked on it.

Now what do we have? We obtain much of what is shown in Figure 2. Figure 2, however, has some additional features:

1) At the very left an additional Y scale has been drawn, which shows some of the values of Y that we are interested in.

2) We notice that all the points (dots) marking the values of Y lie in one straight line.

3) The line connecting the dots has been drawn. This line is called the *graph* of Y as a function of X.

The graph of any function Y consists of the connected (continuous) curve (in this case a line) which runs through all the points (or dots) that mark the locations of Y values that correspond to X values. This is the definition of a graph.

How to Make a Graph

What is the general procedure (or recipe) for determining and drawing a graph—the graph of any variable Y as a function of a variable X? Here it is:

1) Choose some values of X: X_1, X_2, X_3 ... We will name the ith value X_i.

2) Using the rule which specifies the function, calculate the corresponding values of Y, obtaining Y_1, Y_2, Y_3 ... Y_i corresponds to X_i.

3) On a sheet of paper, mark a horizontal line (which is called the X-axis) and a vertical line (which is called the Y-axis).

4) Choose a beginning mark and units of measurement on the X-axis, which will enable you to represent as dots on that line the X-values you have chosen.

5) Choose a beginning mark and units of measurement on the Y-axis, which will enable you to represent as dots on that line the values of Y that you have calculated.

6) For each X_i that you have, locate the spot straight above it or straight below it, which is Y_i distant; at

that point put a small dot to mark the location of that point.

7) If (and only if) the function is a smoothly changing (continuous) function, you may draw a smooth curve through and connecting all the small dots.

An example of the result of this process is shown in Figure 3, the graph of the temperature of a day as a function of the time of day.

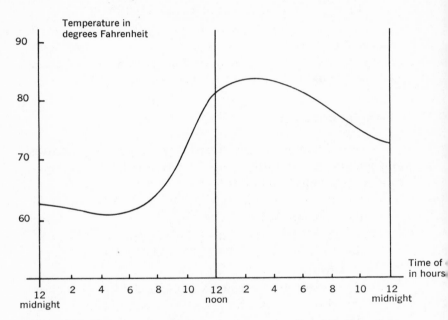

Figure 3. A graph of the temperature of a day as a function of the time of day.

Common Types of Graphs

There are many common types of graphs (see Figure 4). Many graphs are straight lines. Some are circles. Some are curves that look like a series of waves. Every now and then, in the real world, a graph is actually traced by a moving object. For example, a baseball thrown high and then drop-

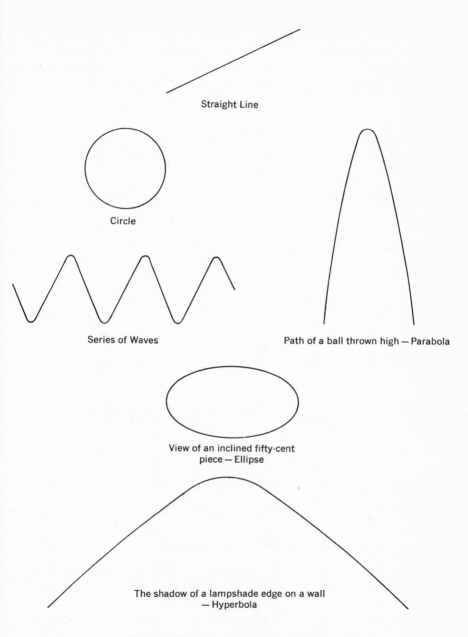

Straight Line

Circle

Series of Waves

Path of a ball thrown high — Parabola

View of an inclined fifty-cent
piece — Ellipse

The shadow of a lampshade edge on a wall
— Hyperbola

Figure 4. Some common types of graphs.

ping again 20 feet away traces a curve that is very close to the graph that is called a parabola. A 50-cent piece looked at from an inclined direction has the visual appearance of a graph called an ellipse. The shadow on the wall of the edge of a round lampshade produced by the lighted lamp may have a shape called a hyperbola.

A common graph is the sawtooth graph. If a boy is compelled to have a haircut every second Saturday, then the length of his hair is a sawtooth graph.

Length of hair Figure 4 (continued)

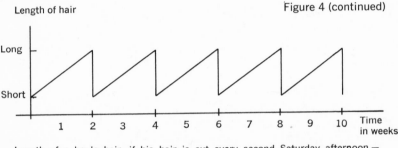

Length of a boy's hair, if his hair is cut every second Saturday afternoon — Sawtooth graph

Graphs have come to be used in many places in the ordinary world of newspapers, magazines, and reports. Graphs of stock-market prices are a common sight. The graph of the trend of the standard of living is often pictured. Even in cartoons a man may be seen looking at a rapidly descending graph and preparing to shoot himself. The graph is a profound mathematical idea that has almost fully emerged from mathematics into ordinary everyday language.

The Particular Function First Graphed

Before we leave our function $Y = 9/5\,X + 32$ and its graph, let us ask, "Why did we choose this function? Is it important? Does it have any use?"

It *is* important. It is the rule whereby a temperature X expressed in degrees Centigrade is converted into a temperature Y expressed in degrees Fahrenheit. The tempera-

ture 32 degrees Fahrenheit, at which water freezes, corresponds to 0 degrees on the Centigrade scale. The
temperature 212 degrees Fahrenheit, at which water boils,
corresponds to 100 degrees on the Centigrade scale. All the
temperatures on the scales, whether within, above, or below
this range, are related by this same rule, which is established
in the science of physics.

Temperature in the physical world reports the average
amount of random motion of molecules. Accordingly, there
exists a state where there is no motion of molecules. This
temperature is −273 degrees Centigrade, or −459.4 degrees
Fahrenheit. For matter to be at a temperature lower than
this is physically impossible. But the formula $Y = 9/5 \, X + 32$
does not express this bottom temperature; for example, the
formula would not stop me from inserting $X = -1000$ and
calculating Y, etc. Here is pointed up again the usual dis-
crepancy between the physical world and the mathematical
world: a mathematical relation may apply fairly well over
a range in the physical world, but the mathematics by itself
contains no guarantee of applicability in the real world outside of that range if unsupported by relevant observations.

A great deal more can be said about functions and graphs.
We have touched very lightly on two of the most interesting
and most important ideas of mathematics. We have not carefully defined these ideas here; instead we have named them,
given examples of them, and talked a little about them. This
kind of treatment is reasonable for an introduction, for persuading you, an intelligent nonmathematician, that these
ideas are not hard to understand and are in many ways partly
familiar to you already. The purpose of this kind of introduction is to remove the roaring lions along the path, and
make it easy for you to feel comfortable with these ideas and
ready to find out more about them. In the same way, when
you first come across such a term as "evolution," or "system,"
or "machine," you find out part of the meaning to begin with,
and gradually, as time passes, more and more.

Derivatives

12

WE HAVE NOW REACHED the place where it makes sense
to explain and try to make clear two of the most important
thousand-horsepower ideas in all of mathematics. These
two ideas are usually not explained to students of mathematics until they begin to study the branch of mathematics
called calculus. This is regrettable. These ideas are not very
hard to understand if a person is interested and can focus his
attention. They bear the names of *derivative* and *integral*.

A good deal of unnecessary mystery and fear has sprung
up around these words. Yet everybody who has reached the
age of reflection already has had many experiences with the
meanings of these words; but usually there has been no one
at his elbow to point out the connections.

We shall take up *derivative* in this chapter and *integral*
in the next.

The Idea:
Rate of Change in Language, Derivative in Mathematics

Perhaps the best thing we can do in order to explain
derivative is to gather pieces of information about it and put
them down. In this way, the idea to which this term refers
gradually becomes clear and well formed in the mind of the
person learning, instead of vague and shadowy.

Here, then, are some true statements about the idea
derivative (each statement being tagged with its classifica-

tion according to the list Commonest Properties and Relations in Chapter 3, page 50):

1) A derivative is a rate of change of something.

[6. SPECIES]

2) For example, if a train is traveling at 60 miles an hour over a certain stretch of railroad, then the rate at which the *distance* changes as *time* changes (i.e., the train's *speed*) is a derivative. In this case the derivative is a constant rate, 60 miles per hour.

[3. EXAMPLE]

3) If a missile is rising faster and faster into the sky, its distance from the ground is continually increasing, and the rate of change of the *distance* as *time* changes (the upward *speed* of the missile) is a derivative. In this case the derivative is not a constant rate, but an increasing rate (at least at the start).

[3. EXAMPLE]

4) If water is flowing through a faucet into a bathtub at the rate of a gallon every ten seconds, then the rate of change of the *volume* of the water in the bathtub as *time* changes is a derivative. In this case the derivative is a constant rate of *flow*, six gallons per minute or 1/10 gallon per second.

[3. EXAMPLE]

5) But if, instead of the volume, we consider the height of the water in the bathtub as the water flows in, and how that *height* changes as *time* changes (remembering the odd shapes of bathtubs to suit the shapes of human beings), then the rate of change of the height as time changes is also a derivative — but this derivative is not a constant. In fact, this rate of change behaves quite irregularly.

[3. EXAMPLE]

6) A derivative *D* is a function which depends on (is derived from) another function *F* in a certain way.

[6. SPECIES]

7) A derivative is not an average rate of change but an instantaneous rate of change. [7. PROPERTY]

8) If we have a function F of an independent variable x, then the derivative D of F with respect to x is the instantaneous rate of change of F as x changes. [5. DEFINITION]

9a) In the example of the train, F is distance traveled by the train as a function of time, and D is its speed, 60 miles an hour;

9b) In the example of the missile, F is the distance traveled by the missile upward from the ground as the time changes, and D is the speed upward of the missile;

9c) In the example of the bathtub, the first F is the volume of water in the bathtub as a function of time, and D is the constant rate of flow, six gallons per minute;

9d) But the second F is the height of water in the bathtub as a function of time and D is the rate at which this height changes, and this is not a constant rate. [5. SIGNIFICANCE OF THE DEFINITION IN THE EXAMPLES]

Calculating Derivatives by Just Looking

Now, so far, we have defined and illustrated derivatives, but we have not calculated any derivatives, except in the case where they were constant numbers, since the rate of change was then constant. But how do we calculate derivatives?

Suppose we take three simple functions of x and examine how we would go about finding their derivatives.

For the first function, let us take $1/3\ x$ (read "one third of x"). For the second function, let us take 2 1/2 (read "two and a half"), a constant for every value of x. For the third function, let us take $1/10\ x^2$ (read "1/10 of x squared" or "1/10 of x times x"). Let's name these three functions the

First Function, the Second Function, and the Third Function respectively.

Let us begin by constructing the graphs of these three functions so as to see how they behave. In Table 1, we choose some simple values of *x* for each function, and calculate corresponding values of *y* making use of the formula

TABLE 1

First Function $y = 1/3\ x$		Second Function $y = 2\ 1/2$		Third Function $y = 1/10\ x^2$	
Chosen Values of *x*	Calculated Values of *y*	Chosen Values of *x*	Calculated Values of *y*	Chosen Values of *x*	Calculated Values of *y*
0	0	0	$2\frac{1}{2}$	1	0.1
3	1	5	$2\frac{1}{2}$	2	0.4
6	2	10	$2\frac{1}{2}$	3	0.9
9	3	15	$2\frac{1}{2}$	4	1.6
12	4			5	2.5
				6	3.6
				7	4.9
				8	6.4
				9	8.1

for the function. In Figure 5 we take those calculated pairs of values *x* and *y* for each function, locate them on the graph as points, and then we draw a smooth curve through them.

Now looking at Figure 5 (pages 170-71) we can see how these three functions behave. The First Function rises smoothly and steadily as *x* increases. Its rate of change is a constant, 1/3 unit of *y* to each unit of *x*. The Second Function is simply a constant—it does not change as *x* changes; its rate of change, therefore, is zero. But the Third Function, in the region of the values where we have drawn it, rises faster and faster as *x* increases, and its rate of change is evidently an increasing rate, different at each point.

In a moment we shall pay some more attention to the Third Function, but first notice that we have calculated two derivatives by just looking. The First Function is a straight line; we can tell its instantaneous rate of change, because its

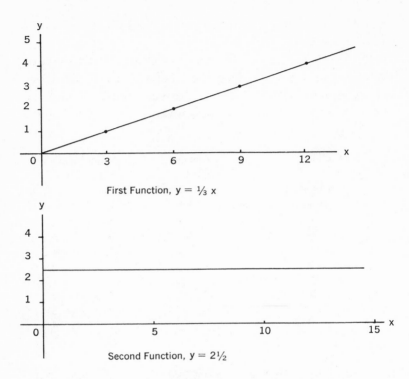

Figure 5. Three sample functions.

rate of change is everywhere the same. The Second Function is still easier: it is unchanging, and so its derivative is zero. This is generally true: at any point where a function is not changing, its derivative is zero.

Think of a marble rolling around in a spherical bowl. The function *F* in this case may be the height of the marble in the bowl, depending on the location (from side to side, and forward and back) of the marble. The marble will come to rest at the lowest point of the bowl. At that lowest point, the point of minimum height, the rate of change of height as the marble moves slightly on its way to stopping (the derivative of the height) is practically zero.

Calculating Derivatives by Estimating

Let us come back now to the Third Function and take another look at it. It is rather a smooth curve; and it does not seem to change its inclination very fast. Can't we estimate the derivative, the instantaneous rate of change?

Let us take for example the point where x equals 6. The curve between x equals 5 and x equals 7 changes its curvature rather slowly. Why not draw a straight line through the points on the curve at x equals 5 (P_1) and x equals 7 (P_2), find the inclination of that sloping line (L), and then use that as an estimate of the instantaneous rate of change at the point where x equals 6? Let's try it.

To find the inclination of that sloping line, it is convenient to draw two lines. One is a horizontal line starting at P_1 (see Figure 5) which is equal in length to the 2 units

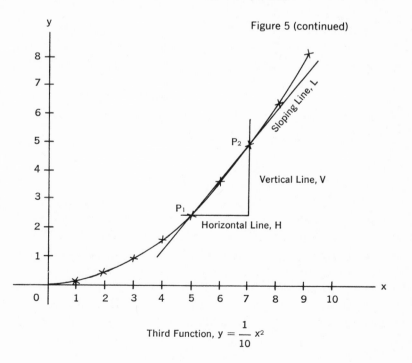

Figure 5 (continued)

$$\text{Third Function, } y = \frac{1}{10}\,x^2$$

from x equals 5 to x equals 7; the second is a vertical line through P_2 (see Figure 5) which is equal in length to the distance between 2.5 (the value of y where x equals 5) and 4.9 (the value of y where x equals 7), and so its length is 2.4. The sloping line therefore rises by 2.4 while it passes over the distance 2. So we estimate the rate of change at x equals 6 as 2.4 divided by 2, which comes out as 1.2. In this way, we estimate the instantaneous rate of change of y at the point where x equals 6 to be 1.2. In other words, at that point we estimate that y is increasing about 20 percent faster than x is increasing: our estimated derivative at that point is 1.2.

The process we have just gone through is the same as applying the rule:

> The average rate of change from one x-unit before a point to one x-unit after such a point is a reasonable estimate of the instantaneous rate of change at the point itself.

How close is our estimate?

More mathematics, which we shall not go into here, shows that the estimate in this case is completely accurate. This is unusual, of course, and it would not ordinarily happen. But also, more mathematics (which we shall not go into here) shows that the approximation by applying this rule is in a great many cases very good.

Calculating Derivatives by Algebra

Clearly it would be useful to have a more general process for calculating derivatives than the two processes we have just used, the first process being Just Looking and the second process being Estimating. Could we not calculate the derivative of the Third Function not just at the point where x is 6, but anywhere? And suppose we had any function at all—how would we go about finding its derivative?

There is a standard accurate algebraic process for calculating a derivative. This process is the same for all functions, both simple and complicated. And most of the process is quite easy to describe (using a little algebra) and to understand (although some important points, mathematically speaking, are left out in the present explanation).

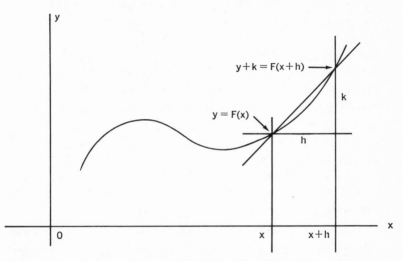

Figure 6. Finding the derivative for almost any kind of function, $y = F(x)$.

Suppose we start with almost any kind of function F of x, written $F(x)$ (see Figure 6). Let us consider it in the interval from x to x plus h, where h is a small quantity. We put x plus h (i.e., $x + h$) into the formula of the function, and we calculate what F becomes using the value $x + h$. This result is $F(x + h)$. We now subtract F of x from F of $x + h$ and we call this difference k. k is the amount of change (or difference) in F when h is the amount of change (or difference) in x. And the average rate of change of F over the interval is k divided by h, k/h.

But this result is only an average rate of change, not an instantaneous rate of change. What shall we do?

We look at the formula, the particular algebra that expresses k divided by h. We try to see what k divided by h becomes as h becomes smaller and smaller and smaller.

Often (but not always) it is very easy for anyone to see just what k divided by h will become, as h becomes smaller and smaller and smaller. Let us take an example.

Suppose that F is the Third Function, one tenth of the square of x, $1/10\ x^2$. Then $F(x+h)$ is equal to $1/10\ (x+h)^2$. By algebra this is equal to $1/10\ x^2 + 2/10\ xh + 1/10\ h^2$. k is equal to $F(x+h)$ minus $F(x)$, and this is equal to $1/10\ x^2 + 2/10\ xh + 1/10\ h^2$ minus $1/10\ x^2$, and this equals $2/10\ xh + 1/10\ h^2$. k divided by h is therefore equal to $2/10\ xh + 1/10\ h^2$ divided by h, and this equals $2/10\ x + 1/10\ h$, or $1/5\ x + 1/10\ h$. Now let h become smaller and smaller and smaller. What will happen to k/h? Why, clearly it will become closer and closer and closer to $1/5\ x$. And so we have calculated the derivative, the instantaneous rate of change of $1/10\ x^2$ with respect to x, in the general case for any x. The derivative equals $1/5\ x$. In particular, if x equals 6, the derivative equals $1/5$ of 6, or 1.2, just as we estimated earlier.

To make perfectly clear what we have just done in these rather fast-traveling paragraphs, let us go back over each step, as if we were cooking according to a recipe, or carrying out a sequence of instructions on a computer (see Table 2).

Let us try this same process in regard to the train example on page 167. Suppose the start of the good stretch of railroad

TABLE 2

No.	Instruction	Step
1	Originally:	At x, F is $1/10\ x^2$
2	Add a small bit h:	At $x + h$, F is $1/10\ (x + h)^2$
3	Subtracting:	In the interval h, the change in F (i.e., k) equals $1/10\ (x + h)^2$ minus $1/10\ x^2$
4	Simplifying:	The change k reduces to $2/10\ xh + 1/10\ h^2$
5	Dividing by h:	The quotient k/h equals $2/10\ x + 1/10\ h$
6	Let h become smaller and smaller and smaller indefinitely:	k/h becomes $2/10\ x$, because h becomes vanishingly small and disappears

is 35 miles from Portland. And suppose we measure time x in hours from the start of the train on that stretch of railroad. Then during the time that the train is traveling down that stretch of railroad, the total distance in miles at any time x that the train has traveled is $35 + 60\ x$. Now, to find the derivative, see the process summarized in Table 3, below.

TABLE 3

No.	Instruction	Step
1	Originally:	At x, the distance traveled is $35 + 60\ x$
2	Add a small bit h:	At $x + h$, the distance traveled is $35 + 60\ (x + h)$
3	Subtracting:	In the interval h, the change in the distance traveled (k) is $[35 + 60\ (x + h)] - [35 + 60\ x]$
4	Simplifying:	The change k reduces to $60\ h$
5	Dividing by h:	The quotient k/h equals $60\ h$ divided by h, or 60
6	Let h become smaller and smaller and smaller indefinitely:	k/h still equals 60

So again we have computed the derivative, and again we show (as of course we knew in this case when we started) that the instantaneous rate of change of the distance traveled by the train as time changes (i.e., the speed of the train) is 60 miles per hour.

What Is the Meaning of a Derivative?

As a result of this portion of the discussion, we can now put down a final statement about the idea *derivative:*

A derivative of a function is the result of two processes:

a. Finding the rate of change of the function over an interval;

b. Letting the interval become smaller and smaller and smaller indefinitely.   [5. DEFINITION]

This is the operational meaning of an instantaneous rate of change. This is how we find a derivative. These two processes are completely general, and the cookbook recipe or procedure set forth in Table 2 and Table 3 will work in all ordinary cases. (I say "ordinary" because mathematicians can find cases where the processes won't work, but these cases are unusual.)

Once again we emphasize that the experience of every human being includes experience with changes and rates of change. For example, when we prepare to cross a street, we make judgments about the speeds of oncoming cars, their rates of change of distance with respect to time. When we play a game of soccer or basketball, we judge not only the speeds of players but the speed of the ball, the rate of change of distance with respect to time.

Of course, most human beings do not know the mathematical language for talking about rates of change. But this is no reason for believing that the mathematical language cannot be understood in terms of our common everyday experiences. Instead, we may have a feeling of discovery and triumph: "Oh, so a derivative is an instantaneous rate of change, and I have been dealing with such things all my life!"

In a way, this insight is like discovering the meaning of a six-syllable word like "responsibility." We learn about responsibilities long before we learn the word itself. A child who learns finally to come when his mother calls has learned a responsibility for coming when she calls. And long before we learn the word "derivative," we have had experiences dealing with rates of change and instantaneous rates of change.

Integrals

WE ARE NOW GOING TO EXPLAIN an idea of mathematics
which is really a ten-thousand horsepower idea. The idea,
with its applications, reaches all through our lives and experiences in the common everyday world in an implicit or
hidden way: we use the idea over and over and we do not
notice it. In fact, this idea is almost like the air we breathe:
we use it every day and pay almost no attention to it. In
addition, the idea and its applications reach all through every
branch of science and engineering in an explicit or obvious
way: because there the word "integral" is used, and there
the sign of the idea

$$\int$$

is used in formulas which describe situations. This sign
comes from an old script capital S, and refers to the fact that
an integral is a kind of a sum, a kind of a summing up.

13

The Idea:
"Summing Up" in Language, "Integral" in Mathematics

Now let us do the same thing about the idea *integral* as
we did about the idea *derivative*—let us gather pieces of

177

information about it until the idea becomes clear and well formed and solidly based.

Here are some true statements about the idea *integral* (each with its classification according to the list Commonest Properties and Relations on page 50):

 1) An integral is a kind of a summing up.

[6. SPECIES]

 2) An integral is the inverse or opposite of a derivative — in much the same way as division is the inverse or opposite of multiplication.   [9. OPPOSITES]

Inverse or Opposite

Here it is worth interrupting the listing of properties of integral in order to explain exactly how the inverse or opposite occurs. To begin with an analogy, let us consider a problem involving the area of a room:

How are area, length, and width related to each other? We know that:

(area) EQUALS (length) TIMES (width)

Now, how do we find length, given area and width? How do we find width, given area and length? The two answers are:

(length) EQUALS (area) DIVIDED BY (width)

(width) EQUALS (area) DIVIDED BY (length)

We say that DIVIDED BY is the inverse or opposite of TIMES.

Returning now to the inverse or opposite of derivative, let us consider a problem involving distance, time, and speed. How are they related to each other? We know from the discussion in Chapter 12 that:

(speed) IS THE INSTANTANEOUS RATE OF CHANGE OF (distance) WITH RESPECT TO (time)

Or we can say — and it is just the same assertion expressed in other words —

(*speed*) EQUALS THE DERIVATIVE OF (*distance*) WITH RESPECT TO (*time*)

This is a good answer if we know *distance* as a function of *time*. But in the real world the problem does not always come that way. Sometimes the problem is:

> Given *speed* as a function of *time*, what is *distance* traveled?

Sometimes the problem is:

> Given *speed* as a function of *distance*, what is the *time* spent?

How do we handle these other two versions of the problem?

We change mathematically the statement about speed as a derivative into other forms of statement that directly answer these questions. But if we do this, we run into the idea of *integral*. Using that idea, in advance of explaining it more fully below, we have these answers:

> (*distance*) EQUALS THE INTEGRAL OF (*speed*) WITH RESPECT TO (*time*);
>
> (*time*) EQUALS THE INTEGRAL OF [ONE DIVIDED BY (*speed*)] WITH RESPECT TO (*distance*)

In this way INTEGRAL is the inverse or opposite to DERIVATIVE.

Some Properties of an Integral

Returning now to collecting true statements about the idea *integral*, which we began to do on page 178:

> 3) An integral *I* is a function that depends on another function *F* in a certain way.   [6. SPECIES]
>
> 4) The integral *I* is a result of a process called integrating performed on a function *F*.
> [18. PRODUCT OF AN ACTIVITY]
>
> 5) For an example, to integrate *speed* with respect to *time* and get *distance* is the result of:
>> (1) breaking up an interval of time into a number of small bits,   (2) summing up all the small distances that we get by taking each bit of *time* and multiplying by the *speed* which applied in that

bit of time; and (3) letting the bits of time get smaller and smaller and smaller, and letting the number of them get larger and larger and larger, indefinitely. [3. EXAMPLE]

An Example of an Integral

As a fuller example, let us think of traveling in a motor car. Suppose we start out at 9:30 on a fine Sunday morning, travel two miles out through crowded streets to a super-highway, go up to high speed, travel for a half hour, then come down from the superhighway and go three miles through country to a friend's house, arrive there, and stop. Let us put into Table 1 the facts we have just talked about, together with a little amplification.

TABLE 1

Stage (1)	Time of: Starting (2)	Stopping (3)	Minutes elapsed = (3) − (2) (4)	Miles per hour (5)	Average Speed: Miles per minute = (5) ÷ 60 (6)	Distance traveled in miles = (4) × (6) (7)
1 City	9:30	9:38	8	15	.250	2.0
2 Super-highway	9:38	10:08	30	55	.917	27.5
3 Country Roads	10:08	10:14	6	30	.500	3.0
All	9:30	10:14	44	44.3	.739	32.5

Time has gone on smoothly from 9:30 to 10:14, for a total of 44 minutes. *Speed* is only roughly shown in the table — our actual speed at any instant has been what the speedometer showed instant by instant as we drove along. The actual *distance* we have traveled up to any moment has been: each scrap of *time* multiplied by the *speed* applicable to that scrap of time, totaled for all the scraps of time from 9:30 on up to that moment. In fact, the actual distance traveled up to any moment is shown by the mileage indicator or *odometer* contained in the same instrument with the speedometer; it usually shows miles and tenths of miles. To make the odometer work, a device inside it sums up all the little bits of distance traveled and thus gives the mileage we have traveled up to any moment. Of course, we have to notice what the odometer shows at 9:30 when starting on our trip because that is the base figure from which it goes forward. The 32.5 miles total distance we have traveled is the *integral* of our actual instantaneous speed with respect to time, from 9:30 to 10:14.

More Examples of Integrals

Another vivid example of *integral* and *integrating* is contained in the experience of any person who has watched a bathtub fill with water from a faucet. Here is the relation:

(The volume of water at any moment in the tub) IS THE INTEGRAL OF (the instantaneous rate of flow into the tub) WITH RESPECT TO (time)

Suppose you are watching masons putting bricks together to make a wall:

(The amount of wall built at any time) IS THE INTEGRAL OF (the rate of putting bricks into it) WITH RESPECT TO (time)

Suppose you are heating a pot of stew on a stove:

(The amount of heat in the pot) IS THE INTEGRAL OF (the rate of heating the pot) WITH RESPECT TO (time)

Think of the earth turning on its axis for two hours, and the line of sunlight at dawn (where the sun changes night into day) sweeping over the earth:

(The additional amount of surface of the earth lighted up in those two hours by the sun) IS THE INTEGRAL OF (the line of sunlight at dawn) WITH RESPECT TO (the amount of turning of the earth)

Suppose you are mowing a lawn:

(The amount of lawn mowed up to any moment) IS THE INTEGRAL OF (the rate of mowing the lawn) WITH RESPECT TO (time)

Think of any two rather irregular curves lying in a plane (see Figure 7):

> (The area between them from a chosen beginning line *B* up to a stopping line *L*) IS THE INTEGRAL OF (the distance *Y* between the curves) WITH RESPECT TO (the distance *X* from the beginning line *B* up to the stopping line *L*)

More Properties of an Integral

With all these examples in front of us, we now go back to collecting true statements, begun on page 178:

6) Whenever there is a rate or a flow, the result of its operation over a period of time is an integral.

[18. PRODUCT OF AN ACTIVITY]

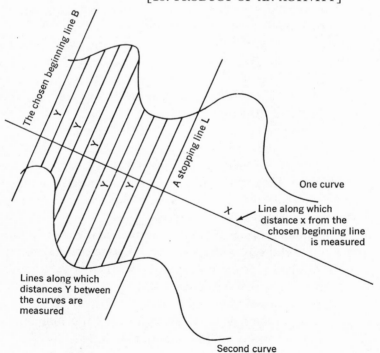

Figure 7. An area between two rather irregular curves.

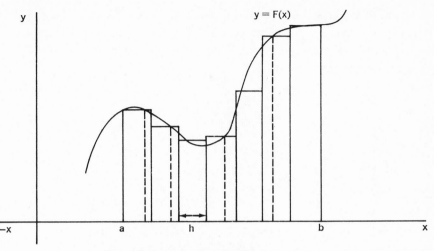

Figure 8. A rough approximation to an area.

7) And in the general case, the integral from a to b of any function F with respect to x is the result of four steps:

   a) Breaking up the interval from a to b into a number of small bits, each of length approximately h.

   b) Multiplying an approximate value of F in that interval by h, to get F times h for that interval, which is an approximate sum or area for that interval;

   c) Adding up all the different little sums or areas so obtained, and

   d) Letting the length of the bits become smaller and·smaller and smaller, and the number of them become larger and larger and larger, indefinitely.   [5. DEFINITION]

8) The integral of a function y is equal to the exact area under the curve y, from the beginning of integrating to the end of integrating. [7. PROPERTY]

To see what all this means, let us look at Figure 8. We see a function $F(x)$, and the interval from a to b, and a number of small bits of the interval, each with a width h, and some typical heights of the function *F* drawn with dashed lines in some of the intervals. We could come fairly close to the whole area (the integral) by adding up the area of all the small pieces shown.

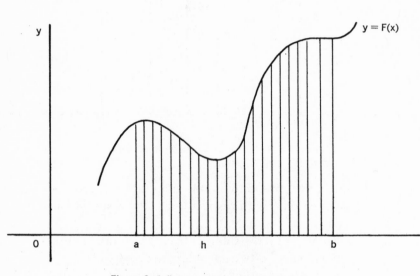

Figure 9. A finer approximation to an area.

Now let us look at Figure 9. We see exactly the same function (the same curve) and just the same interval from *a* to *b*, but here there are about three times as many bits in the interval, and the width of the bits (the new *h*) is only about one third of the previous width (the old *h*). To get the heights of the little slices of area, we can imagine vertical dashed lines of length equal to some middle height in the slice. Now with this change we can come much closer still to determining the whole area (the integral) by finding the sum of the three-times-as-many small pieces of area shown.

The whole area (the exact integral) is what you obtain if the width of the small slices becomes smaller and smaller and smaller, and the number of them becomes larger and larger and larger, indefinitely.

How to Calculate an Integral by Just Multiplying

So far, we have defined and illustrated integrals, but we have not said much about calculating them.

We can in some cases calculate an integral by just multiplying. In any case where a speed is constant, or a flow is constant, or the function we want to integrate is constant, then the integral is the result of multiplying only.

Take for example the Second Function in Table 1 and Figure 5 of Chapter 12, where y equals $2\frac{1}{2}$, a constant value. The integral of y with respect to x is simply y times the length of the interval of x from the beginning of integrating to the end of integrating.

For example (see Figure 10), if we start at x equals 1.2 and go on to x equals 4.9, then the integral is equal to $2\frac{1}{2}$ times the difference 4.9 less 1.2 or 3.7, and the result is 9.25.

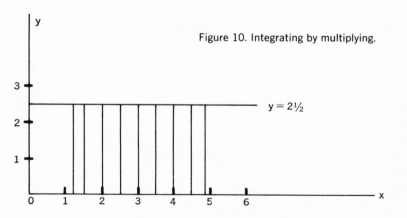

Figure 10. Integrating by multiplying.

$y = 2\frac{1}{2}$

The integral of the function $y = 2\frac{1}{2}$, from x equals 1.2 to x equals 4.9, is equal to 3.7 times 2.5, or 9.25.

In fact, we can see that in this case we have computed the area under the line $y = 2\frac{1}{2}$ from the point where x equals 1.2 to the point where x equals 4.9.

How to Calculate an Integral by Estimating an Area

Now let us take a look at the First Function (see Figure 5, Chapter 12), where y equals 1/3 x. Suppose we want the integral of this function from x equals 3.2 to x equals 8.8. This is equal to the marked area (see Figure 11) under the straight line y equals 1/3 x down to the x-axis. How shall we find this area?

Well, the easiest thing to do is to draw the middle vertical line (call it M) of this area, and swing the little triangle T, sticking up at the right, around the middle point so that it fills in the equal space marked S. Thus we change the area into a rectangle, and the area is equal to the length times the middle height. In this case, it will be equal to the length, $8.8 - 3.2 = 5.6$, times the middle height, exactly 2. Multiplying, the answer is 11.2.

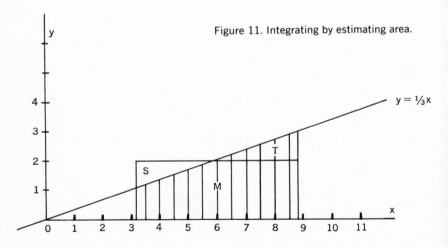

Figure 11. Integrating by estimating area.

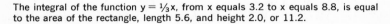

The integral of the function $y = \frac{1}{3}x$, from x equals 3.2 to x equals 8.8, is equal to the area of the rectangle, length 5.6, and height 2.0, or 11.2.

How close is our estimate? In this instance it can be shown by more mathematics, such as reasoning taken from geometry, that the estimate is exactly right.

In fact, in any case where we are finding an area under a straight line y, this kind of reasoning will give us the correct answer. It amounts to using this multiplication rule:

(The integral of the height of the straight line function y from a to b) EQUALS (the distance from a to b) TIMES (the height of the line y calculated at the point halfway between a and b)

Finally, suppose we have the case of the Third Function (see Chapter 12), y equal to 1/10 of the square of x. Suppose we want the integral of this function from x equal to 1.5 to x equal to 8.5 (see Figure 12). This is equal to the area under

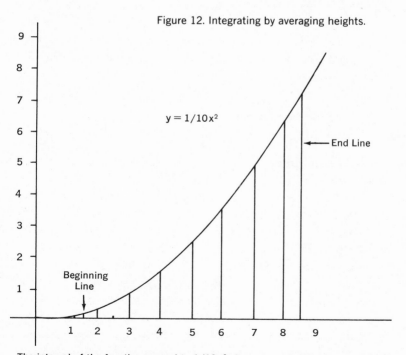

Figure 12. Integrating by averaging heights.

$y = 1/10x^2$

End Line

Beginning Line

The integral of the function y equal to $1/10x^2$, from x equals 1.5 up to x equals 8.5, is equal to the area under the curve from x equal to 1.5 up to x equals 8.5. The area can be estimated by taking the average of all the heights at 2, 3, 4, 5, 6, 7 and 8, and multiplying by the length of the base line from 1.5 to 8.5.

the curve from x equal to 1.5 up to x equal to 8.5. How shall we find this area?

It is obviously not a good idea to use only the middle height, which will underestimate. Nor is it a good idea to use only the two end heights, which will overestimate. Suppose however we take all the heights of the curve at the points where x equals 2, 3, 4, 5, 6, 7, 8, average these heights, take that average as the representative height, and multiply by the length of the area, the distance from x equal to 1.5 to x equal to 8.5, which is 7.

Here is the calculation:

1/7 of $(0.4 + 0.9 + 1.6 + 2.5 + 3.6 + 4.9 + 6.4)$ times 7
One seventh of seven is one, and so we have left only the sum of the heights, which is 20.3. This is our estimate of the area (the integral); it ought to be quite close.

Clearly, there is another general rule expressible here:

(The integral of y from a to b) EQUALS APPROXI-MATELY (the sum of the y's calculated at unit intervals from a to b)

Calculating Integrals by Algebra

Clearly, it would be useful to have a more general way for calculating integrals than the two processes we have just used, Just Multiplying and Estimating Areas. It would be good to have an exact method for obtaining a formula that would compute the area under any curve y equal to any function F of x. This would be equivalent to having a formula that would express the integral of any function.

But for this problem mathematicians to date have to report failure. There is no known direct method for integrating *any* kind of function. Furthermore, the main result of three hundred years of mathematicians' searching is the doubt that any such method exists. Of course, for a great many kinds of functions and for many important functions, exact-formula integrals have been figured out.

TABLE 2

(1)	(2)	(3)	(4)
		Exact	Resulting
	Formula for	Formula for	Exact Formula for Area
Function	the Function	Its Integral	Under the Curve from a to b
First	$y = 1/3\ x$	$x^2/6$	$b^2/6 - a^2/6$
Second	$y = 2\frac{1}{2}$	$2\frac{1}{2}x$	$2\frac{1}{2}b - 2\frac{1}{2}a$
Third	$y = 1/10\ x^2$	$x^3/30$	$b^3/30 - a^3/30$

For example, for our First Function, y equal to 1/3 of x, and for our Second Function, y equal to $2\frac{1}{2}$, and for our Third Function, y equal to 1/10 of the square of x, exact-formula integrals have been figured out by mathematicians. The formulas are shown in columns 3 and 4 of Table 2, above.

What does the formula in column 3 mean? This formula is like the mileage reading on the odometer; it tells you that if you know your starting point and your ending point, you can get the mileage of your trip by subtracting. In the same way, if the starting point from which you measure area is a, and the ending point b, then, if you put a and b into the formula and subtract, you get the area. See column 4 of Table 2, where this process has been carried out.

How do these accurate integrals compare with the estimates we previously worked out (pages 185, 186, 188)? The comparison is shown in Table 3, below. Two of the estimates are exactly correct. The third one is too small by only

TABLE 3

Function	Particular Value of a	Particular Value of b	Arithmetical Result of the Formula	Previous Estimate	Discrepancy, Equal to Formula Result Minus Estimate
First	3.2	8.8	$(8.8)^2/6 - (3.2)^2/6$ $= 77.44/6 - 10.24/6$ $= 67.2/6 = 11.2$	11.2	none
Second	1.2	4.9	$2\frac{1}{2}(4.9) - 2\frac{1}{2}(1.2)$ $= 9.25$	9.25	none
Third	1.5	8.5	$(8.5)^3/30 - (1.5)^3/30$ $= 614.125/30 - 3.375/30$ $= 20.358\ldots$	20.3	.058 ... or 3/10 of 1%

3/10 of 1 percent! These results are not bad. In fact, they are an excellent illustration of the fact that if you understand the principle of an idea, and can make reasonable estimates, you can go a very long way.

But what about the cases where you cannot find an exact-formula integral?

If the function you want to integrate is not included in the collection of exact-formula integrals that mathematicians have found and described, it would be reasonable for you to give up and use approximate methods instead. This is not a severe penalty, because for almost all the functions that occur in the real world, or that anyone is interested in, you can obtain numerical approximations to integrals as close as you please. Often the numerical accuracy you can get is far greater than the accuracy of the observations in the physical situation that gave rise to your integral. Especially if you have an automatic computing machine available to do some calculating for you, you can get along very well with numerical-approximation methods.

The Applications of Derivatives and Integrals

With these explanations of the ideas of derivative and integral behind us, we are perhaps able to begin to see how and to what extent these ideas permeate exact thinking wherever exact thinking occurs. Every determination of an average rate, when we are thinking also of the possibility of an instantaneous rate, approaches the idea of a derivative. Every addition, every summing up of a large number of small items, where the individual items become smaller and smaller and smaller but we are summing up more and more and more of them all the time—every operation of this kind comes closer and closer to the idea of an integral.

For example, the volume of an irregularly shaped solid is an example of an integral. Presumably, if a surface that surrounds a part of space is described to us, we can calculate the volume. Calculation of this volume would be equivalent to integrating once, twice, or three times.

In many branches of science, such as physics, mechanics, chemistry, biology, and many others, when processes are being studied, there are many problems involving the behavior of distance, time, speed, volume, electrical current, weight, acceleration, and many other physical quantities.

Examples of such problems are:
1) What are the various angles to which a gun should be raised in order that it may shoot various distances?
2) If an airplane flies in a direction always at the same angle from the north, how much farther will it travel than if it flew along the shortest path? (A path on a globe always at the same angle from the north is called a *loxodrome*, and a shortest path is called a *great circle*.)
3) How should a rotating mass be supported so that it will have the least vibration when it turns fast?
4) How should an electric motor be constructed so that it can lift and lower various weights?

In many physical problems such as these, the answer is not a single number but a formula. In any of these problems, what we want to do is find a formula so that any one of the quantities may be calculated, given the behavior of the other quantities. In any of these problems where an instantaneous rate enters, the derivative of a function is involved. In any of these problems where the result of summing up the behavior of a variable is involved, then the integral of a function is involved. It is in this way that derivatives and integrals permeate a great many of the equations of the exact sciences.

In the 1600's, when men were considering carefully the problems of explaining the motion of the planets and other mechanical motions, the European mathematicians Isaac Newton and G. W. Leibnitz, independently of each other, discovered the principles and operations involving derivatives and integrals. We can now see that even if these great men had not discovered them then, it was inevitable that human beings, pressed on by the problems that had to be solved, would before long have discovered the concepts of derivative and integral.

Note:
The Symbols Used in Mathematics for "Derivative" and "Integral"

Although it is not a necessary part of the present explanation, it may be useful to report the symbols used in mathematics for designating derivatives and integrals. Then a reader will be able to translate from the symbols he may find in a mathematical explanation into the ideas explained in this chapter.

To designate the derivative of a function f of x, mathematics uses:

$D_x f$ (read "dx of f"), or

$\dfrac{df}{dx}$ (read "df over dx"), or

f'_x (read "f prime sub x")

All these symbols have the same meaning, the instantaneous rate of change of the function f as x changes.

The small d comes from the word "differential" or "difference." The capital D comes from the word "derivative."

To designate the integral of a function f of x, mathematics uses:

$\displaystyle\int_a^b f dx$ (read "integral from a to b of f with respect to x"), or

$\displaystyle\int f dx$ (read "integral $f\,d\,x$" or "integral of f with respect to x")

These two symbols have slightly different meanings.

The first symbol is called the *definite integral*, and refers to the area under the curve f, from x equals a to x equals b.

The second symbol is called the *indefinite integral,* and stands for any function whose derivative with respect to x is f. All such functions are very much alike because they only differ from each other by a constant. For example, the indefinite integrals of the function $1/3\ x$ include $1/6\ x^2 + 13$, or $1/6\ x^2 - 2.36$, or $1/6\ x^2 + 365.28$, etc., because for every one of these functions the derivative is exactly the same, namely $1/3\ x$.

Equations

14

Equations

Of all the kinds of relations in mathematics, one of the
most important, and the most common, is an equation. What
is an equation?

An *equation* is a statement that two expressions are interchangeable — that they stand for the same number (or other
mathematical entity). An equation always has the form of a
statement that something is "equal to" or interchangeable
with something else. Suppose we call the first something X
and the second something Y and translate the words "is
equal to" or "equals" into the usual mathematical sign, "=."
Then an equation always has the form "$X = Y$."

For example, here is an equation:

$$2 + 3 = 5$$

Here is another equation:

$$8 - 2 - 1 = 5$$

A famous axiom about equations is:

Things equal to the same thing are equal to each other.

So, if we wish, we can conclude that $2 + 3$ equals $8 - 2 - 1$,
since $2 + 3$ equals 5 and $8 - 2 - 1$ equals 5. Yet we can easily
see that the three expressions "$2 + 3$," "5," and "$8 - 2 - 1$"
are, of course, all different as expressions. One contains
three symbols, one a single symbol, and the last one five
symbols. But these three expressions all designate, denote,

194

or represent the same quantity, commonly called 5; and the equations assert that $2+3$ and $8-2-1$ are each interchangeable with 5.

These are very simple examples, of course. But we have chosen such simple examples to make clear the essential nature of the idea of an equation.

Of course, if only such simple examples as these occurred, people probably would do nearly all their reasoning with equations by using common sense and would pay little attention to the special operations that one can use on equations. In the same way, people do nearly all their reasoning about the relations expressed by AND, OR, NOT, EXCEPT, IF . . . THEN with common sense, and pay little attention to the interesting fact that an algebra called Boolean algebra handles these ideas precisely and mathematically. But equations and their special properties enable us to handle rather easily many complicated situations and to maneuver adroitly the entities of mathematics and the relations between them. For this reason, equations are very important.

Equations Not Involving Numbers

In the definition of an equation above, we hinted that the mathematical entities in an equation might be not only numbers but also other entities. What are some examples of equations not using numbers?

For example, suppose someone says:

> If tomorrow is Saturday, then day before yesterday is Wednesday.

Here we have two equations:

> Suppose tomorrow equals Saturday.
> Then day before yesterday equals Wednesday.

In this example the expressions "tomorrow," "Saturday," "day before yesterday," "Wednesday" refer to days of the week; and the entities among which equations are stated are the days of the week.

For another example, here is an old conundrum:

A man looking at a picture says "Brothers and sisters have I none, but that man's father is my father's son." Whose picture is the man looking at?

Let's analyze the assertion of the man looking at the picture. Without changing the meaning in any way, we can rewrite the assertion in simpler words:

I have no brothers or sisters, and my father's son is that man's father.

From our knowledge of human relationships, the person:

my father's son (and I have no brothers)

stands for, designates, is interchangeable with, *is equal to:*

I (or me) (and I am a man).

So again we can write an equivalent statement:

I am that man's father.

And this statement is equivalent to an even simpler one:

That man is my son (or one of my sons).

So the picture that the man is looking at is a picture of his son or one of his sons. In this case, persons are the entities among which equations are stated.

Of course, other entities besides numbers, days of the week, and persons may enter equations. Wherever two expressions X and Y can designate the same entity, we can write $X = Y$.

Changing Equations into Other Forms

The relation of equals has turned up previously in some of the mathematical ideas we have been talking about. For example, we talked about a formula "Area equals length times width." It is an equation because of the word "equals" in the statement. Nearly every formula is an equation; but not every equation is a formula.

Now suppose we know the area and the length of a room, and the formula "area equals length times width," but we do not know the width. Can we use the equation to find out the width? The answer is yes.

First, the equation is made completely clear by setting it down as:

area A equals length L times width W,

$A = L \times W$

These three letters, A, L, W, stand for numbers. Since they are numbers, we can treat them as numbers, and we can make use of another very important axiom about equations:

> You can add, subtract, multiply, or divide and in general OPERATE on each side of an equation IN THE SAME WAY, and the result is still an equation.

For example, suppose we know the area A and the length L, but we do not know the width W. In this particular case, we can divide both sides of the above equation by the same number, the number stating the length L. On the left-hand side, we obtain A divided by L, A/L. On the right-hand side we obtain L times W all divided by L, $(L \times W)/L$. This is the same as L divided by L times W, and L divided by L, of course, is one, and one times W is W. So we obtain the new equation:

A divided by L equals W

$A/L = W$

or, writing it the other way around, we obtain:

W equals A divided by L

$W = A/L$

In this way we have found out the width W, which we did not know, in terms of the area A and the length L of the room, which we were given. And in general, over and over again, whenever we have an equation, we can change it around into other forms and so compel it to give answers to our questions.

Equations between Temperature Scales

Here is another example. Consider the equation F equals nine fifths C plus 32:

$F = (9/5)C + 32$

This equation expresses Fahrenheit temperature F as a

function of Centigrade temperature C. For example, if C is 20 degrees, $F = (9/5)20 + 32$. Five divided into 20 goes 4 times, 4 times 9 is 36, 36 and 32 is 68, and so we know that if the Centigrade temperature is 20 degrees, the Fahrenheit temperature is 68 degrees. Since 68 degrees Fahrenheit is approximately room temperature, 20 degrees Centigrade is approximately room temperature. (This is an example of applying "Things equal to the same thing are equal to each other.")

Maneuvering an Equation to Answer a Different Question

Now if we are given the Centigrade temperature, how do we get the Fahrenheit temperature? We can maneuver; we can manipulate, change the equation to find this result.

First, we subtract 32 from each side and we have:

$$F - 32 = (9/5)C$$

Then we multiply both sides by 5, and we have:

$$5(F - 32) = 9C$$

And then we divide both sides by 9, and we obtain:

$$(5/9)\ (F - 32) = C$$

Then we change the order, and say:

$$C = (5/9)\ (F - 32)$$

or, in words, the Centigrade temperature is equal to five ninths of the result of subtracting 32 from the Fahrenheit temperature.

For example, if we have been given a Fahrenheit temperature of 68 degrees, we put the 68 in place of the F, and we find 68 minus 32, which is equal to 36. Then we divide 9 into 36 and we get 4. And then we multiply 4 times 5 and we get 20, which is the corresponding temperature in degrees Centigrade. In this way we see we can start with a Fahrenheit temperature of 68 degrees and calculate the Centigrade temperature of 20 degrees.

The "changed around" or *inverse* equation works truthfully in all the cases that the original equation covers. Our new equation is as general as the equation we started with. We can use one equation to go from Fahrenheit to Centigrade, and the other equation to go from Centigrade to Fahrenheit.

A Problem in the Form of an Equation

Now let us consider the case of a problem in the form of an equation.

PROBLEM 1: Seven times some number plus 14 equals zero. What is the number?

Solution: We start off by saying: let X equal the number. Then the statement in the problem is:

7 times X plus 14 equals 0

$$7X + 14 = 0$$

and our problem is to find X, that is, to *solve* the equation.

In this problem there is just one unknown number X, called briefly an *unknown*; every other number in the equation is known: 7, 14, and 0. In a case like this, it is not another formula or function that we desire to come out with but a single value of X for which the equation is *satisfied*, becomes true. When we find out the value that X has, and substitute its value for X in the equation, then the equation will become exactly true.

What shall we do?

Again we use the same method—operating in just the same way on both sides of the equation. We subtract 14 from both sides of the equation and we obtain:

$$7X + 14 - 14 = 0 - 14$$

The plus 14 and the minus 14 on the left side of the equation cancel, and so the equation reduces to $7X$ equals minus 14:

$$7X = -14$$

To get X by itself on the left side, we divide both sides of the equation by 7:

$$7X/7 = -14/7$$

On the left side we have 7X divided by 7, and on the right side we have minus 14 divided by 7. On the left side the sevens cancel, and we obtain X. Minus 14 divided by 7 is equal to minus 2. So we have the result X equals −2:

$$X = -2$$

Is this answer right?

To verify the answer X equal to minus two, we make a test. We substitute the value minus two for X in the equation, and see if the result is truly an equation. In:

$$7X + 14 = 0$$

we replace X by −2, and we replace = by $\overset{?}{=}$ (meaning "is it equal to?"). We obtain:

(7 times minus 2) plus 14, is it equal to 0?

or in symbols:

$$7(-2) + 14 \overset{?}{=} 0$$

Now seven times minus two is minus 14. And minus 14 plus 14 equals plus 14 minus 14, which equals zero. So the equation verifies. We have proved by substituting that the value we calculated is correct.

The method of substituting an answer to see if it satisfies the original equation is a standard way of testing the correctness of an answer.

Operations

Now you may have already noticed what we do in order to change an equation into other equations, in order that we may get our questions answered. The rule (which we have stated already once) is essentially a simple rule, and yet it is a very powerful rule and deals with all kinds of equations. This is the rule:

> You may perform any operation you want to, on both sides of an equation, and the result will still be an equation, provided you take care to perform exactly the same operation on each side of the equation.

The rule, however, would not be complete unless we

added a warning. Most operations, it is true, produce just one result; and for all these, and only these operations, the rule is good. If, for example, your operation is to add 14 to each side of an equation, the result of adding 14 is unique; and the equation will still be an equation.

But there are operations which have no result and are therefore impossible: "Choose a number which is greater than 4.1 and less than 3.9 and add that to each side of the equation." Of course, there is no such number and that operation cannot be performed.

The most notorious of the impossible operations is dividing by zero. To divide A by B means to find a number Q (for quotient) such that A is equal to B times Q. Therefore, to divide A by zero means to find a number Q such that Q times zero is equal to A. But *for every number*, that number times zero is equal to zero. And so, it is not possible to find a number Q which if multiplied by zero is equal to A. (*Note:* You might say, "What about infinity?" We could, if we wished, adopt a rule that ∞, infinity, should be included as a number. But that does not help here. If we take our equation $X = Y$ and divide each side by zero, the equation changes into $\infty = \infty$, true in all cases, and we cannot go any further at all in solving $X = Y$.)

There are also operations which produce more than one result, and are therefore ambiguous. A famous example of the ambiguous operations is taking a square root, because in general a number has two square roots—and which one is meant?

Suppose you have the equation 4 equals 4, and then you take the square root of both sides. You have on the left side plus or minus 2, and on the right side plus or minus 2, and if you are careless about choosing your signs properly, you get the result that minus 2 is equal to plus 2, and this of course is wrong—not true. Thus the operation of taking the square root may give you an incorrect result. If you perform on each side of an equation an operation that does not produce only a single or unique result, there is no telling what you will wind up with, for your result is no longer a necessarily true equation.

Simultaneous Equations

In addition to a single equation that by itself expresses a problem, we may have two or more equations that have to be solved together in order to solve the problem. We then desire to solve the equations together, i.e., *simultaneously*, so that we know what values of the unknowns will solve all of them at the same time.

For example, suppose we have the following problem:

PROBLEM 2: Twice a certain number and three times a certain other number is equal to 13. Twice the first number and five times the second number is equal to 19. What are these numbers?

Solution: In line with our convenient procedure for solving mathematical problems, let us abbreviate. We say:

"Let the first number be X, and the second number be Y."

Then the first statement becomes:

2 X's plus 3 Y's is 13

and the second statement becomes:

2 X's plus 5 Y's is 19

Rewriting in still simpler style, we have:

$$2X + 3Y = 13$$
$$2X + 5Y = 19$$

Now how do we go about solving these equations?

Well, there is absolutely nothing we can do with just one of the equations that will tell us what both X and Y are. But if we use both equations, there is something that we can do that will tell us: We can subtract the first equation from the second, because then "2 X's" in the first equation will be taken away from "2 X's" in the second equation, and this will make the term containing X disappear in the new result.

Performing this operation, on the left side we have ($2X$ plus $5Y$) minus ($2X$ plus $3Y$), and this is equal to $2X$ minus $2X$ plus $5Y$ minus $3Y$; and, of course, 2 X's minus 2 X's is zero; and 5 Y's minus 3 Y's leaves 2 Y's. On the right-hand side we have 19 minus 13, and this is equal to 6. So the result is:

$$2Y = 6$$

Dividing both sides by two, we have one Y is equal to 3:

$$Y = 3$$

Now we substitute Y equal to 3 in the first equation:

$$2X + 3(3) = 13$$

and so we have 2 X's plus 3 3's equals 13, or 2 X's plus 9 equals 13, and therefore 2 X's equals 13 minus 9, or 4:

$$2X = 13 - 9 = 4$$

and since 2 X's equals 4, one X is equal to 2:

$$X = 2$$

More Simultaneous Equations

The preceding problem, of course, is rather a special case; in most cases a simple subtraction will not cause the term containing the X's to disappear. So let us consider a problem where we have to do something more, such as the following:

PROBLEM 3: There are two numbers X and Y, which have the properties $2X + 3Y = 18$ and $4X + Y = 16$. What are they?

Solution: We desire to solve these equations simultaneously, finding the values of X and Y that will make the first equation true and the second equation true at the same time.

Now as we look at these equations, we can say to ourselves, "Well, if the first equation had $4X$ instead of $2X$ in it, then we could subtract one from the other, and we would get an equation involving Y only, and this we could solve without trouble, because it would be like the previous case."

By doubling both sides of the first equation, we can obtain an equation with $4X$ in it. We, in fact, obtain $4X + 6Y = 36$. The second equation is still $4X + Y = 16$ and we subtract that equation from $4X + 6Y = 36$. If we take $4X$ and a single Y away from $4X$ and $6Y$, we have only $5Y$ left over. If we take 16 away from 36 we have 20 as the result, and so we have the equation $5Y = 20$. Then we divide both sides by 5, and we have $Y = 4$.

Suppose we put $Y = 4$ into the second equation, $4X + Y = 16$. We will then have $4X + 4$ is equal to 16. If we take away 4 from each side, we have $4X$ is equal to 12. If we divide each side by 4, we have X is equal to 3. We have thus solved the pair of equations $2X + 3Y = 18$ and $4X + Y = 16$, which we selected as an example.

Now let us see if the solution $X = 3$, $Y = 4$ is correct. We put 3 and 4 for X and Y in the left side of each of the equations, and see what we obtain. The first left side, $2X + 3Y$, becomes 2 times 3 plus 3 times 4, which equals 6 plus 12, which is 18, which verifies. The second left side, $4X + Y$, becomes 4 times 3 plus 1 times 4, or 12 plus 4, which equals 16, and that equation verifies also. Therefore we have shown by substituting that the values we found for X and Y are correct.

A Practical Problem Requiring Equations

Suppose now that we consider a more interesting problem, the kind of problem which actually might occur in the real world, and in which we must use simultaneous equations in order to solve the problem. Here is such a problem.

PROBLEM 4: A corporation's income before taxes is $1,105,000. The Federal tax is 42 percent of the income after the state tax is deducted. The state tax however is 9 percent of the income after the Federal tax is deducted. Calculate Federal tax, state tax, and income after taxes.

Solution: Suppose we let F equal the Federal tax and S equal the state tax. The problem states that the Federal tax will be equal to the income minus the state tax, all times 0.42. This we can set down in the following equation, (1):

$$F = (1,105,000 - S) \ (0.42) \quad \ldots (1)$$

The problem also states that the state tax is equal to the income minus the Federal tax, all multiplied by 0.09, and this we can put down in the following equation, (2):

$$S = (1,105,000 - F) \ (0.09) \quad \ldots (2)$$

Multiplying by 0.42 in the first equation, we get F equals 464,100 minus 0.42S:

$$F = 464,100 - 0.42S \quad \ldots (3) = 0.42 \ (1)$$

Multiplying by 0.09 in the second equation, we get S equals 99,450 minus 0.09F:

$$S = 99,450 - 0.09F \quad \ldots (4) = 0.09 \ (2)$$

By adding 0.42S to both sides of equation (3), we obtain F plus 0.42S equals 464,100:

$$F + 0.42S = 464,100 \quad \ldots (5) = (3) + 0.42S$$

By adding 0.09F to both sides of equation (4) we obtain S plus 0.09F equals 99,450:

$$S + 0.09F = 99,450 \quad \ldots (6) = (4) + 0.09F$$

Now let us choose one of the unknowns F and S, and try to get rid of it using the same trick we previously used. Suppose we set to work to get rid of the unknown S. Let us multiply equation (6) all the way through by 0.42. Then we get 0.42S plus 0.0378F equals 41,769:

$$0.42S + 0.0378F = 41,769 \quad \ldots (7) = 0.42 \times (6)$$

We are now able to subtract equation (7) from equation (5), causing the terms having S to disappear, that is, getting rid of S. This gives us an equation involving F only:

$$F - 0.0378F = 464,100 - 41,769 \ldots (8) = (5) - (7)$$

We obtain F minus 0.0378F equals 464,100 minus 41,769; and this reduces to 0.9622F equals 422,331:

$$0.9622F = 422,331 \quad \ldots (9)$$

Dividing both sides by 0.9622 (this is easy, of course, only if you have a desk calculating machine at your arm's reach), we find the first answer, what F equals:

$F = 438,922$, to the nearest whole number
Now that we know F, we can find 0.09 of F and put it into equation (4) to find S. 0.09 of F is 39,503 to the nearest whole number. Putting that into equation (4), we have S equals $99,450 - 39,503$, and therefore S equals 59,947 to the nearest whole number.

The proof of correctness can be carried out by substituting $F = 438,922$ and $S = 59,947$ in the original equations (1) and (2), and determining what happens. Equation (1) becomes 1,105,000 minus 59,947, all times 0.42, equals 438,922, as it should. Equation (2) becomes 1,105,000 minus 438,922, all times 0.09, equals 59,947, as it should.

The last question in the problem is the income after taxes. In order to calculate this, we start with 1,105,000, subtract 438,922, the Federal tax, and 59,947, the state tax, and come out with 606,131, as the income after taxes.

A great deal more can be said about equations. Although this is not the place to say all of it, we should remark here that the search for solutions to equations has been a process which has taught mathematicians a great many facts about mathematics that they did not at first know. In other words, just as scientists ask themselves questions about the natural world, and then set themselves experiments which they hope will answer their questions, so mathematicians ask themselves questions about numbers and other entities, usually expressed as equations involving unknowns, and then go hunting for ways to answer the questions. As a result of this process, new kinds of numbers and other mathematical entities, previously unsuspected, have been found. For example, by searching for a number which would satisfy the equation X squared equals minus one, mathematicians devised what they called "imaginary" numbers. Examples are i (the square root of minus one, or $\sqrt{-1}$), $-i$ (minus the square root of minus one), $2\pi i$ (two times pi times the square root of minus one), etc. Later on, it turned out that these so-called "imaginary" numbers were not really imaginary in the sense of having no real existence or application; instead, they have important applications in the real world, as for example in dealing with geometry, rotating motion, and alternating cycle electricity.

Angles

ANOTHER OF THE THOUSAND-HORSEPOWER IDEAS
of mathematics is the concept of *angle* with its closely associated idea of *direction*. Directions and angles are deeply
embedded in human thinking; this is shown in a large number of basic, essential words of language (common preposi-
tions, adverbs, and adjectives) such as "to, from, north, south,
right, left, along, across," and so on. If you search through the
commonest words and phrases of language, you will notice
how many of them refer to directions, angles, and orienta-
tions.

The ancient Greeks became fascinated with the subject
of lines and angles, and out of their studies they developed
a great branch of mathematics dealing with this subject—
geometry. The *Elements of Geometry* put together by the
mathematician Euclid in Alexandria in the third century
A.D. is the best known of all mathematical works; since 1482
it has been printed in more than a thousand editions.
Euclid's presentation stood for over 1500 years as a great
monument to the reasoning power of the human mind. In
the nineteenth century Euclid's presentation of geometry
began to yield to the studies of modern mathematicians,
who increased greatly the rigor of the reasoning in proofs,
founded other branches of geometry (non-Euclidean), and
made other expansions and improvements.

208

In our ordinary everyday world we use a collection of rough and approximate words and ideas about directions and angles. The most important subdivision of this collection contains "forward" and "back," or "one way" and "the opposite way"; this part gives us the concepts of temperature "above zero" and "below zero," and much more. Another part of this collection is the set of the four compass directions, north, east, south, west, together with some simple intermediate angles such as southeast. A third part of this collection is the set of four directions relative to a person: forward, right, backward, left. A fourth part of the collection consists of directions based on clock faces; in a story about air fighting, a pilot can say "the pursuing plane was coming in at four o'clock," and he will be understood as referring to a direction backward and to the right. In grade school we learn to measure angles in right angles, degrees, and fractions; and in our industrialized world full of manufactured goods, we find enormous numbers of right-angled corners. The territory of ideas here outlined is about as far as we go with the directions and angles in the ordinary world. But in mathematics some remarkably important properties of angles and directions appear; they turn out, in fact, to be intimate parts of many numbers.

Angles

Exactly what is an angle?

An *angle* is the amount of opening between two lines that meet each other. The amount of opening is observed and measured in the flat surface (or plane) in which those two lines both lie. For example, in Figure 13, we can think of line *a* as the starting position of the bottom line of a closed door, with its hinge at the point 0, the hinge point (the *vertex*). We then think of the door swinging open, wider and wider and still wider, having successive positions such as line *b*, line *c*, and line *d*, until finally it reaches the position of line *e*. Then the angle is the amount of opening measured from line *a* to line *e*.

An angle *A* can be larger or smaller than another angle *B*. All we have to do to compare them is to match up one line of angle *A* and its hinge point with one line of angle *B* and its hinge point, and then look to see if the other line of angle *A* falls on the farther side or the nearer side of the other line of angle *B*.

But what exactly do we mean by the "amount of opening"? How shall we measure it? For example, how should we go about measuring the amount of opening, the angle, between two lines such as line *a* and line *e* in Figure 13?

How to Measure an Angle

One way to measure the angle is by means of a circle with its center at the hinge of the door. Suppose that *P* is a black spot on the bottom of the door. Then, as the door swings open, the point *P* will trace out a part of a circle, called an *arc* of the circle. And if the door were made so that it could swing completely around on its hinge, then the point *P* would trace out an accurate and complete circle.

Now suppose that instead of just any circle, we choose a circle of standard size, say a circle with radius of one unit. Then if we could measure the arc on the circle of standard size from one line of an angle to the other line of the angle,

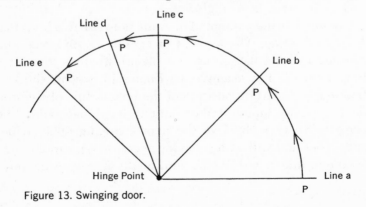

Figure 13. Swinging door.

we would have a standard measure of the amount of opening between the two lines. One angle will be greater than, or less than, another angle according to whether the standard arc of the first angle is greater than, or less than, the standard arc of the second angle. One angle will be twice another angle if the standard arc of the first angle is twice the standard arc of the second angle.

Babylonian Measurement of Angles

All this was apparently first realized by the Babylonians over 4000 years ago. What they did in order to measure angles was to take any whole circle and divide it first into six equal divisions. Then they divided each of these six divisions into 60 equal parts (called *degrees*); then they divided each degree into 60 equal parts (called *minutes*); and then they divided each minute into 60 equal parts (called *seconds*). And ever since that time, people, being conservative, have been dividing the circle, for angle-measuring purposes, in just the same way. This angle-measuring system is one of the most ancient parts of human culture.

It is easy to express this method of measuring angles in a simple measuring instrument. This instrument is called a *protractor*, and a picture of it is shown in Figure 14. To measure with it, we take the protractor and match up the

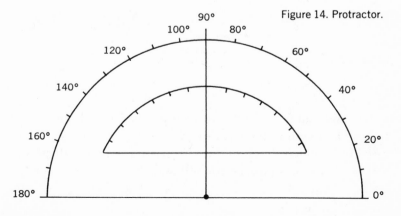

Figure 14. Protractor.

zero line on the graduated circle with one line of the angle we desire to measure (in Figure 13, this is line *a*). Then we make the hinge of the angle (in Figure 13, this is the point 0) coincide with the center of the protractor circle. Then we observe where the other line of the angle (in Figure 13, line *e*) crosses the graduated circle, and we read off in degrees and fractions the amount of the opening between the two lines. The measurement turns out in this case to be about 137 degrees.

This is a good sensible way for measuring many angles, in the same way that using a carpenter's six-foot folding ruler is a good sensible way for measuring many distances. A great deal of the time the method works easily and well.

Specification of Angles — Slope

There is another important and useful way of specifying angles. This way makes use of what is called the *slope* of a line. The slope of a line is equal to:

(the vertical rise or fall of the line) DIVIDED BY (the corresponding horizontal distance).

For example, if a road has a slope of 1/6, then the road rises vertically one foot in every six feet of horizontal distance, or 16 2/3 feet in every hundred feet (see Figure 15). There we see an inclined "road" (the sloping line) which cuts

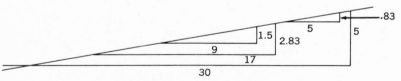

Figure 15. Road with an upgrade of one in six.

across and makes an angle with various horizontal reference lines. The sloping line rises one unit of height for every six units of distance. Each of the four triangles shown displays this fact. For example, the triangle with a horizontal distance of 9 units has a vertical height of 1.5 units, which is one sixth; etc. From the picture it is clear that no matter how many horizontal lines or vertical lines we draw, the rise of the road, which equals:

(the length of any vertical height) DIVIDED BY (the length of the associated horizontal distance)

will always be the same, 1/6. The "clearness" is, of course, not proof. Mathematically, we should demonstrate this statement by a rigorous argument.

How to Estimate an Angle from the Slope Using a Table

But how do we go from the slope of a line L to the angle a that it makes with a horizontal?

There are several ways. One way is to look in a table of answers previously figured out by mathematicians. This is called a table of "natural tangents." An extract from such a table is shown in the table below, which will tell us the angle that corresponds to the slope of 1/6 that we were talking about a moment ago:

Slopes (or Natural Tangents) — Sample

Slope or Natural Tangent	Differences	Corresponding Angle in Degrees	Differences
.1584	.0018	9.00	.10
.1602	.0018	9.10	.10
.1620	.0018	9.20	.10
.1638	.0018	9.30	.10
.1656	.0017	9.40	.10
.1673	.0018	9.50	.10
.1691	.0018	9.60	.10
.1709	.0018	9.70	.10
.1727	.0018	9.80	.10
.1745		9.90	

How do we use this table?

The table tells us that for a slope of .1584 (see the first

column), the corresponding angle is 9.00 degrees (see the third column), and similarly, for a slope of .1602 the corresponding angle is 9.10 degrees. But the slope that we are interested in is 1/6, or expressed as a decimal, .1667. We look down the table and we notice that this number .1667 lies between the slope .1656 for the angle of 9.40 degrees (fifth line in the table) and the slope .1673 for the angle of 9.50 degrees (sixth line in the table), and so the angle we want to determine is between 9.40 degrees and 9.50 degrees.

What would the proper angle be? Well, the difference between .1656 and .1667 is .0011, and the difference between .1656 and .1673 is .0017. The slope we are interested in is .1667, which is clearly .0011/.0017 or 11/17 of the way from .1656 to .1673. So it would be very natural to estimate that the corresponding angle is 11/17 of the way from 9.40 degrees to 9.50 degrees, which would be 9.40 degrees plus 11/17 of .10 of a degree, or approximately .06. From this reasoning, the angle for the slope of 1/6 is very close to 9.40 degrees plus .06, or 9.46 degrees.

The method we have just used for finding an angle not listed in the table for a slope that is not listed in the table is a powerful approximate method that is commonly employed and is usually satisfactory. It is particularly satisfactory when the values in the table are changing very smoothly, which is the case here, as you may see if you look in the second and fourth columns, which show the changes, the differences, in the successive values of the numbers in the first and third columns, respectively. As we mentioned in Chapter 11, the name of this method is *linear interpolation*, because the method uses "interpolating" or "putting between," and because it assumes that the change in one variable is proportional to the change in the other variable.

Now for us to look in a table of natural tangents would be a very good system for finding angles if all of us walked around with tables of natural tangents in our pockets — but we don't! Also, an adequate table of natural tangents would have to be bulkier by far than the short extract shown here. Is there any neater way whereby, knowing a slope, we can calculate an angle?

Yes, there is another way, but it involves several formulas and rules to be used together, and a little more work in understanding ideas. It is however a neat trick that saves you forever from having to walk around with a table of natural tangents in your pocket if you wish to estimate angles from slopes.

First, we have to understand another unit in which angles may be measured; this is called the "natural" unit, or radian.

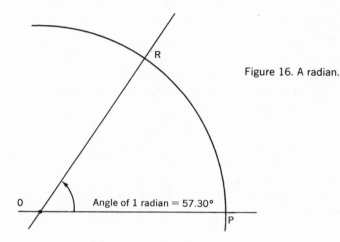

Figure 16. A radian.

Angle of 1 radian = 57.30°

The radius OP equals the radius OR and equals the arc PR.

Measurement of Angles in Radians

If we take a circle and mark off along the curve of the circle a distance equal in length to a radius of a circle (see Figure 16), then we have at the center of the circle an angle which corresponds to or is measured by an arc equal to the radius. This angle is called a *radian*.

Now, of course, it is hard to "bend" a radius neatly and exactly so that it conforms precisely to the curvature of the circle; if you should try to do this in the physical world, you would never know if you had really succeeded, and different people would get different results. But we can calculate easily what the result would be because we know that the circumference of a circle equals two pi times the radius. Pi (π, 3.14159265 . . .) is a famous number which in the last few years has been calculated to more than 4000 decimal places by means of automatic computers. Since the number of degrees in a whole circle, or 360 degrees, is equal to two pi radians, one radian expressed in degrees will be equal to 360 divided by two pi, and this divides out to be about 57.30 degrees (the 0 in this case is a significant figure, because more accurately the figure is 57.296 degrees). Therefore, for any given angle the formula will be:

> (number of radians) IS EQUAL TO (number of degrees) DIVIDED BY 57.30, or
> (number of degrees) IS EQUAL TO (number of radians) TIMES 57.30

The name *radian* was adopted about 1879 because many calculations about angles become much simpler with this "natural" choice for the unit of angular measure, while the Babylonian degree is, of course, arbitrary, without a scientific basis in mathematics.

How to Estimate an Angle from the Slope Using a Formula

Now let's come back to the problem of a neat quick formula to obtain an angle, given its slope. Here is the formula:

> For small angles (we shall come back later to what meaning should be given to "small"):
> (the angle in radians) IS ALMOST EXACTLY EQUAL TO (the slope)

If we should want instead the angle in degrees:

For small angles,
(the angle in degrees) IS ALMOST EXACTLY EQUAL TO (the slope) TIMES 57.30

For example, let's take the case where the slope is 1/6. What is the angle in degrees? Using the second formula,
(the number of degrees in the angle) IS ALMOST EXACTLY EQUAL TO (the slope 1/6) TIMES 57.30

Multiplying 1/6 by 57.30 we have 9.55 degrees as the approximate angle. We previously found out that the angle was 9.46 degrees. Clearly, 9.55 degrees is really close; it is only about 1 percent too large. This is certainly close enough for most practical purposes.

To what extent can we use this formula? In other words, how small is "small" in the above formula?

One thing we can say right away: for all angles smaller than about 9½ degrees and for all slopes smaller than 1/6, the error will not be more than 1 percent; and the formula will be no less accurate. If we take a look at Figure 17, we can see a good reason why this is true: for small angles, the arc of the circle (the angle in radians since the radius is unity) is very close to the length of the line at the right stretching up (the slope for the angle, since the horizontal distance is unity). The section of circle in the shape of a small piece of pie clearly shows that as the angle becomes smaller and smaller, the arc of the circle and the line touching the circle going vertically up become more and more equal in length—although clearly the line will always be a little bit longer than the arc.

Can we correct the formula, by finding out some correction to subtract?

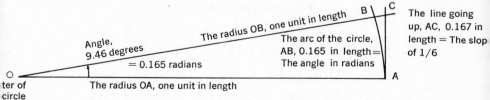

Figure 17. Closeness of slope and arc.

A More Accurate Formula for an Angle

There is a more accurate formula, and we shall now put it down without discussing where it came from, an interesting story but a bit complicated. Let x be the length of the vertical line touching the circle and going up; when the radius is 1, the length of this line is numerically equal to the slope of the angle—just as the length of the arc is numerically equal to the angle in radians. Here is the formula:

For slopes less than 1:

(the angle in radians) IS EQUAL TO $x - x^3/3 + x^5/5 + \ldots$

Only a small amount of calculation using this formula is needed to find out angles for slopes up to about 1/2. To calculate angles efficiently for slopes larger than 1/2 and less than 1, and for slopes larger than 1, other formulas and rules are needed; to explain them here will take us too far afield.

Now let us see if this more accurate formula works properly in our example, that is, if it will give us the correction we want for the angle for slope 1/6. All we shall need is a part of the formula: $x - x^3/3$, because if $x = 1/6$, then the first term dropped is $x^5/5 = 1 \div (6 \cdot 6 \cdot 6 \cdot 6 \cdot 5) = 1/38880$, which is so small that it will not affect our answer. $x^3/3$ is equal to $1/(216 \cdot 3)$, and this is equal to 1/648. Then $x - x^3/3$ equals .16667 − .00154, which equals .16513. Multiplying by 57.30 to change from radians to degrees, we get 9.462 degrees; and this is fine confirmation of our previous answer.

So much for the discussion of angles, the way they are measured, slopes, and how we can get angles from slopes. Let us pay some attention now to the subject of directions, angles measured from a fixed reference line.

Directions and Numbers

In our discussion of numbers so far, we have talked about numbers which were either positive numbers, like $3\frac{1}{2}$ or

765.2, or negative numbers, like −9.832, or zero, which is neither positive nor negative. In other words, we have been content with numbers which express size or magnitude, and either no direction (if we have been talking only about positive numbers) or else one of two opposite directions (if we have been talking about both positive and negative numbers).

But what about still other directions? If positive numbers represent "to the right," and negative numbers "to the left," then what about forward and back? and up and down? and diagonally?

Direction in one way or the opposite way has been combined with numbers so that we have positive numbers and negative numbers. In the same way, the multitude of other directions that exist in the real world can be combined with numbers, and we obtain what are called directed numbers or *vectors*. We can have vectors in two dimensions — any direction in a plane. We can have vectors in three dimensions — any direction in space. And mathematicians have invented and found uses for vectors in four and more dimensions; such vectors are often necessary for dealing with many types of problems involving motions, forces, strains, etc.

How directions and numbers may in general be combined we shall now consider.

Four Directions

To begin with, we look at a straight line running to the right and to the left of where we are standing (see Figure 18). Let's call this line "Main Street." We choose a point on the line close by us, and we say "We choose this point as the point from which we shall start our measurements to the right and to the left." The usual name of this point is the *origin* (in the sense of the original beginning for measurements); we label it *zero* (0). The direction to the right of

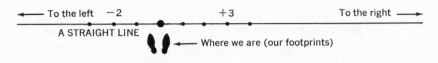

Figure 18. Two directions on Main Street.

this point we shall call the *positive direction*, and the direction to the left of this point we shall call the *negative direction*. We choose a *unit distance*, a convenient measuring rod (see Figure 18). Then the point one unit to the right of the origin bears the label plus one (+1, or plain 1). And the point one unit to the left of the origin bears the label minus one (−1). The number plus three, for example, is the label of the point three units to the right of the zero point; the number minus four is the label of the point four units to the left of the zero point.

Next, we take a second straight line — let us call it "Broadway"— running forward and backward from where we are standing. We make it pass right through the zero point, and we make it lie at right angles to our first line (see Figure 19). Clearly, we can measure distances forward from the zero point in what we may consider a new positive direction, and

Figure 19. Four directions, Main Street and Broadway.

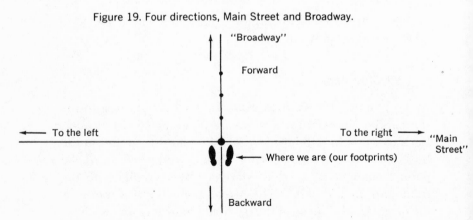

measure distances backward from the zero point in what we may call a new negative direction.

But instead of using 1 to refer to one unit forward, and −1 to refer to one unit backward, let us adopt the letter i to refer to one unit forward along Broadway and $−i$ to refer to one unit backward along Broadway. Then all the points on Broadway can be labeled as multiples of the units plus i or minus i. For example, the point 3.78 units forward from the origin (0) can be labeled 3.78 times i, or 3.78 i. To arrive there, we take the forward unit i and multiply it by 3.78.

But this product, 3.78 i, is also i times 3.78. The point 3.78 is found on Main Street at a point 3.78 units to the right from zero. To multiply it by i seems to be the same as moving the point by a turn through a right angle so that it coincides with the point 3.78 i on Broadway. Therefore we can say, "To multiply by i is the same as to turn through one right angle" (counterclockwise, i.e., in the direction contrary to the way the hands of a clock turn).

Now suppose we multiply 3.78i by i once more. This should mean that the point labeled 3.78i is shifted another right angle counterclockwise; so that now we find that 3.78i times i (or 3.78i^2) coincides with the point −3.78 on Main Street, to the left of the origin.

If 3.78 times i times i equals −3.78, then i times i equals −1. This is the same as saying i squared (i^2) equals −1 (minus one): $i^2 = -1$.

If we take the square root of both sides, then i is equal to plus or minus the square root of minus one:

$$i = +\sqrt{-1} \quad \text{or} \quad -\sqrt{-1}$$

Thus, incidentally, we have found an answer to one of the old riddles of algebra: positive numbers squared give positive numbers; negative numbers squared give positive numbers; therefore what kind of numbers when squared give the negative numbers? Answer: numbers with i, squared, give the negative numbers.

In the same way as multiplying by *i* represents a counter-clockwise turn of 90 degrees, so multiplying by i^2 (equals -1) should represent a counterclockwise turn of 180 degrees. And -1 times -1 represents a counterclockwise turn of 180 degrees plus another counterclockwise turn of 180 degrees, or a total of 360 (or 0) degrees, giving $+1$. At last we have a reasonable explanation of the rule in elementary algebra that "minus times minus is plus."

The letter *i*, which is the first letter of the word "imaginary," is a memorial to the time when mathematicians needed and invented such numbers but did not realize that they could label points on the perpendicular line. And so they called the square roots of negative numbers "imaginary numbers," and they called ordinary positive and negative numbers "real numbers." Of course, all these numbers are in fact no more imaginary and no more real than ordinary numbers like 2 or 7.

Many Directions

We are now ready to look over the rest of the flat surface or plane in which the two lines Main Street and Broadway are embedded. But perhaps now we can call those lines by their regular names: Main Street is regularly called the *axis of reals* and Broadway is called the *axis of imaginaries*. The numbers that lie on the axis of reals (Main Street) are called the *real numbers*, and the numbers that lie on the axis of imaginaries (Broadway) are called the *imaginary numbers*. What kinds of numbers lie in the rest of the plane?

It turns out that all the rest of the points in the plane (see Figure 20) can be labeled as the sum of a real number and an imaginary number. For example, $-3-2i$ is to be found by going three units to the left from zero, and then two units backward from that point.

The plane is called the *complex plane*, and the numbers for which it provides locations are called the *complex num-*

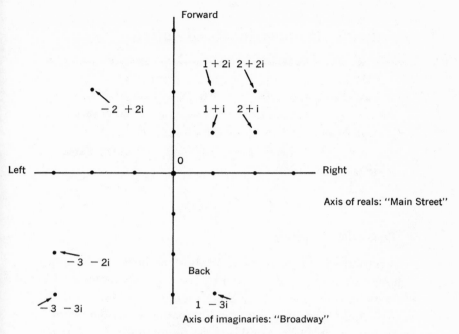

Figure 20. The entire "city" on the plane.

bers. Of course, these numbers are hardly complex in the everyday sense of being very complicated; but the name has been used for a long time, and by the term "complex numbers" mathematicians mean those numbers which can be located here and there all over the plane.

A great deal more can be said about angles and directed numbers. But perhaps enough has been said here to give a reasonable introduction to these basic concepts of mathematics.

Logic: Properties and Relations

16

Reasoning Correctly

Up to this point we have described mathematics to some extent, but we have so far said very little about logic. To some people logic is part of mathematics; to other people it is something more basic than mathematics, of which mathematics is a part, and out of which mathematics is developed. Which viewpoint is held is often a matter of taste, but the second viewpoint has more to be said for it.

What is logic?

Logic is essentially the subject of how to reason correctly, how to proceed correctly from some statements to other statements. Let us take a famous example. If:

    all men are mortal

and if:

    "mortal" means "will eventually die"

and if:

    you and I are men (i.e., human beings)

then:

    I will eventually die

and:

    you will eventually die

and:

    all human beings we know will eventually die.

224

Factual Truth vs. Logical Truth

Is it factually true that all human beings will eventually die? With the extraordinary increase of knowledge in the modern world, the possibility exists that one day men will understand enough about biochemistry and other sciences so that some men will eventually be able to live, and not only live but stay in good health, as long as they choose to.

This possibility of perpetual youth and immortality fascinated the ancient Greeks; it is still a theme for modern novels, such as James Hilton's *Lost Horizon*, the story of Shangri-La, a land where people never grew old. But even if men should be able to change ordinary human lifetime from 80 years to 200 years, a thousand years is a long time and a million years is much longer still, and it seems quite doubtful, to say the least, that any man will live as long as a million years.

This discussion emphasizes two important and contrasting kinds of truth: One is *factual truth*, which is tested by comparing it with the real world, with observations that men, particularly scientists, can make, with facts as observed in the real world. The other kind of truth is *logical truth*, which is tested by the correctness or validity of the process of reasoning from one statement to another statement: "If all men are mortal, and Socrates is a man, then Socrates is mortal."

Factual truths, the summaries of observations about the real world which have been made up to the present time and have been generalized to the future, admit of errors. In other words, one more observation may be the exception that shows that a certain summary of prior observations is not correct.

Logical truths, valid deductions from assumptions or postulates, do not admit of errors or exceptions. In other words, an exception proves that a statement thought logically true is actually not logically true. If the sum of one and one and one is precisely three, and no other number, then the sum of one and one and one cannot be 2.99 or 3.001 or any number except three. If a "logical conclusion" is tested against an "exception," and the exception holds, then the "logical conclusion" is false and has to be scrapped, discarded.

Our Experience with Logic

Let us take another example. Here are three statements:
1) That speck up in the sky is a hawk.
2) All hawks are birds.
3) All birds have feathers.
Therefore:
4) That speck up in the sky has feathers.

This is an example of correct reasoning, reasoning in accordance with the principles of logic. We are unable to see the speck up in the sky in detail. But we can deduce that it has feathers. The procedure for taking three statements of this particular kind of pattern (1, 2, 3), and producing from them a conclusion statement of the pattern (4), is one of the procedures studied in the subject of logic.

From these examples and our experiences with reasoning processes, we can see that we use logic nearly all the time in nearly all the sentences that we say or think. Almost everybody, in fact, uses logic; certainly almost everybody is able to use logic much better than he can explain or understand it. Using logic is something like walking; most of the time we walk without thinking about it, and most of the time we use logic without thinking about it. We make our sentences hang together logically, we avoid contradicting ourselves, without thinking about how to make this happen.

But every now and then, because of lack of consciously understanding and using logic, we make serious logical mistakes and produce a great deal of trouble for ourselves.

The Content and Vocabulary of Logic

Our familiarity with logic is shown in the vocabulary of ordinary everyday words. The content of logic is expressed in many (though not all) of the commonest words and phrases of language:

yes	the	a, an	it	to	if
no	of	another	kind	for	and
some	in	there is	sort	by	or
all	same	such	thing	with	else
none	different	has	which	is a	except

A word by itself usually has more than one meaning, and sometimes when out of context, the multiple meanings conflict. And so, in the study of logic, we need to examine phrases using these words and identify precisely the logical ideas being expressed.

The content of logic is also expressed in the following terms:

- statements, sentences, propositions
- truth, falsity, assertion, denial
- reasoning, implications, theorems, proofs
- things, individuals, elements
- classes, groups, collections, types
- properties
- relations

The Parts of Logic

Logic has a number of parts.

One part consists of the rules for *deduction*, the process in which you start with some statements called *premises* and proceed correctly to other statements called *conclusions*. If your method of deducing is correct, and if your premises are true, your conclusions are guaranteed to be true. The four sentences written above about the speck in the sky are a good example of deduction. The speck in the sky is too high up for us to see at first hand whether or not it has feathers; but we can *deduce* that it has feathers.

A second part of logic is called *induction*. It deals with drawing conclusions from examples, instances, cases, observations, evidence. Logic does not guarantee that conclusions derived by induction are entirely and completely true. For example, by logical induction from the experience of human beings, we can assert the statement:

The sun will rise tomorrow.

But we can never be sure that this statement will remain true. In fact, scientists have predicted that given a long enough time, the sun will not rise "tomorrow"; the current prediction is that in something like ten billion more years the sun will undergo a severe nuclear explosion, and the heat and radiation from this explosion will consume the earth.

A third important part of logic is the study of logical fallacies — well-recognized methods used by human beings (such as politicians) for persuading themselves or their listeners that certain statements follow from other statements, when actually they do not.

For example, one famous kind of fallacy is called *argumentum ad hominem* or argument based on the kind of man who states the argument. This line of attack on a statement is based on asserting that the truth of a statement is to be judged by the kind of man who says it. For example:

"Oh, you can't believe Hamilton Jones. He is very unreliable — what he says just can't be true."

This kind of argument is incorrect, fallacious, wrong, because even an unreliable person is likely to speak truth some of the time. In fact, it is quite difficult for any person to speak in such a way that every single statement he makes is false. Even if Hamilton Jones speaks falsehoods 95 percent of the time, and is therefore very unreliable, any given statement of his must logically be judged on its own merits.

How Is Logic Related to Mathematics?

Logic is related to mathematics in a profound way: it is the foundation on which mathematics is erected. In fact, all of mathematics may be deduced logically from a very few (less than two dozen) primitive and fundamental ideas of logic. Here are some of these ideas:

1) *Inclusion:* . . . is a _____; as in "A horse is an animal."
   —the relation of inclusion of something in a group or set or class
2) *Conjunction:* . . . and _____; as in "Beauty is tall and Beauty is black."
   —the operation of joining two statements together so that both are asserted
3) *Negation:* not _____; as in "Lad is not black," or "It's not true that Lad is black."
   —the operation of denying or negating a statement
4) *Plural:* _____s, meaning plural, as in "horses."
   —an operation that makes classes, groups, collections or sets
5) *Truth Values:* yes, meaning "That's true"; and
                    no, meaning "That's not so."
   —an operation which reports whether a statement is true or false.

Some of the most important ideas of mathematics, such as the idea of a variable and the idea of a formula, are just as important in logic. In fact, the application to logic of powerful ideas that were originally worked out for mathematics has produced what is called *mathematical logic* or *symbolic logic*.

Properties

In logic there are some ideas which are powerful aids in

organizing one's understanding and unlocking information in any field of knowledge.

One of these ideas is the idea of a *property* or attribute. For example, in the statement (any paraphrase is acceptable):

> *x* has feathers, or
> *x* is feathered, or
> *x* is a thing which has feathers, or
> *x* is a thing which is feathered, or
> *x* is a feathered thing

we are asserting that *x* has a certain property, the property of having feathers.

In symbols, to say that *x* has the property P, we write:

> *x* P

To say that *x* is a thing which has the property P, we give the name C to the class of things which has the property P, and we write:

> *x* ϵ C

The sign ϵ (which is a Greek epsilon) stands for "is a member of," "is an element of," "is a," "is one of."

These two ways of talking in logic, xP and $x\epsilon C$, are interchangeable.

This situation in logic is very much like the situation in grammar with subject and predicate. A subject corresponds to *x*. A predicate corresponds to P; it is regularly a property, something which can be asserted as belonging to something else, the subject. In general, almost all adjectives and a great many common nouns express properties or classes.

In logic, it is agreed that if one class, C, has exactly the same members as another class, C', then those two classes, C and C', are identical, are precisely the same. But a property P and another property, P', even though all the things which have the property P may be exactly the same as all the things which have the property P', are not necessarily interchangeable. For example, in logic, the *null class* is *the* class which has no members at all. There exist no unicorns, and there exist no dodos, and there exist no triangles with four sides. So the class of unicorns is the null class, and the class of dodos is the null class, and the class of triangles with four sides is the null class, and these classes are all equal to each other. But the property of being a unicorn and the property of being a dodo and the property of being a triangle with four sides are different properties.

We do not expect a thing to have the property P and not have the property P at one and the same time. A law of logic, attributed to Aristotle, called the Law of the Excluded Middle asserts:

Everything is either A or not-A.

A great deal of the time this is true.

For example:

A foot is either 12 inches long or it is not.

However, in applying this sort of logical rule in the real world, we find many ticklish cases where we have to be careful to identify what we are talking about, and to identify just what property we are referring to. For example:

Either my boy David is good or my boy David is not good.

Actually, of course, David has a whole spectrum of behavior, and some of it may be good sometimes and some of it may be bad sometimes. Fortunately, in mathematics we have many easy applications like:

The number 2 is even or it is not even.

Checklists, Forms, and Definitions

One of the convenient applications of the notion of property is making a checklist (or filling in a form), a list of questions and points for checking off to make sure that some task with all its ramifications has been really completed.

For example, a form for applying for a job always has a number of spaces provided for answers to questions; and in those spaces the applicant fills in his answers appropriately. Each answer consists of a report on a certain property or characteristic of the person applying: last employer, length of time employed, nature of duties there, are properties of the previous employment of the person; schools attended, years in which attended, major courses studied, marks in such courses, are properties of the prior education of the person.

In defining a strange term, the gathering together of its distinguishing properties serves as a definition. For example:

An aardvark is a large nocturnal burrowing mammal of Africa, living largely on termites, and having a long extensile tongue, claws, and conspicuously long ears. Its body is three to four feet long. Its name comes from South African Dutch "aard" meaning "earth," and "vark" meaning "pig."

Relations

Another of the important ideas of logic is the idea of a relation (or association or connection) between something and something else. All the following are relations:

1) x is the father of y.
2) x is greater than y.
3) x caught y.
4) x is the brother or sister of y.
5) x is a subdivision of y.
6) The members of x can be exactly matched up or paired one by one with the members of y.

In general, we can write xRy meaning "x has the relation R to y."

What is the definition of a relation? We can say that the relation R is defined if, for every pair of values of x and y presented, we can decide (or believe we can decide) whether the statement "x has the relation R to y" is true or false.

In mathematics, and in logic, we are interested in the abstract properties of relations, because from some relations we can deduce others. For example, if a relation is *transitive*, then if xRy and yRz, it is true in all cases that xRz.

For example, "is a descendant of" is a transitive relation, and "is greater than" is a transitive relation, and equality is a transitive relation. But "is next to" is not a transitive relation, and "is a parent of" is not a transitive relation, and "is on top of" is not a transitive relation.

The relations so far mentioned have been *two-termed*: that is, the relation is of the form " . . . has the relation R to ——" and this has two blanks to be filled in with two terms. But it is not necessary that relations be two-termed. Some relations are three-termed: "x is between y and z," *betweenness*, is a three-termed relation. Some relations are four-termed. *Exchange*, A exchanges X with B in return for Y, is a four-termed relation. For example:

"I will give you \$1 for your new kitten"

is a four-termed relation involving four entities: two persons and two things (if we treat the kitten as a thing).

Matching or Pairing

A kind of relation which is of very great importance in mathematics is relation number 6 above, called "one-to-one correspondence"—the relation of matching or pairing together two collections or sets. The matching relation is used when we count: we match counted objects with the uttered words "one, two, three, four, five . . . " In this way we can decide if the number of members in some group is the same as the number of members in some other group. If we run out of members of one group before we run out of members of the other group, then the second group has a greater number of members than the first group.

But this process is not limited to counting. For example, the numbers:

1, 2, 3, 4, 5, 6, 7, 8, 9, 10 . . .

can be matched up with or paired with the numbers:

2, 4, 6, 8, 10, 12, 14, 16, 18, 20 . . .

by agreeing that the rule for finding any number in the second series is to double the corresponding number in the first series.

Number and Infinity

Suppose we agree that the relation:

"the class x has the same number of elements as the class y"

is true if and only if the members of x can be matched up with or paired with the members of y by making use of some rule.

If we so agree, then:

the number of all the whole numbers 1, 2, 3, 4, 5, 6 . . .

is the same as

the number of the even numbers, 2, 4, 6, 8, 10, 12 . . .

How can it be that only part of a class, the even numbers, has the same number of members as all of the class, the whole numbers, 1, 2, 3, 4, 5, 6 . . .?

Such a class is *infinite*. It is true of infinite classes that a part of the class can be matched up with the whole class.

Do such classes exist in the real world? No, they do not. If the whole known universe 6 billion light years in radius were jam-packed tight with the smallest known particles, protons, less than 10^{130} protons would be needed. This is a number *much smaller* than infinity!

But the idea of infinite classes simplifies the structure of mathematics and makes it more systematic, tidy, and beautiful to mathematicians.

Statistics:
Probability and Frequency Distributions

17

Tossing a Penny 50 Times - Probability—First Approach - Increasing the Number of Experiments - The Results of Many Experiments - Probability—Second Approach - Frequency Distributions - Bias - Repeatability

TWO MORE THOUSAND-HORSEPOWER IDEAS OF MATHEMATICS come from the field of probability and statistics: the idea of *probability* and the idea of *frequency distribution.*

All our lives we use these ideas, often without clearly understanding more than a little about them. We look at the weather, and we say, "Probably it is going to rain tomorrow." We talk of how people behave, and we say, "Harry is late much more often than he is on time." We discuss the outcome of a football game, and we say, "According to the newspaper, the odds are seven to three that Princeton will beat Columbia next week."

Such statements reflect the ideas of probability and statistics. Many words and phrases in common everyday use refer to this area of mathematics:

probably	often	almost always
perhaps	seldom	almost never
maybe	frequently	the chance is good that . . .
likely	rarely	certainly

In this chapter we take some steps toward finding out the mathematical meaning of the two ideas *probability* and *frequency distribution.*

Tossing a Penny 50 Times

One of the commonest situations where probability shows its nature is tossing a coin. Suppose we make an experiment.

Take a penny out of your pocket and look at it carefully. One side bears heads, and the other side bears tails. Each side seems to be pratically flat; at any rate, the slight bulges of the design in relief are just abѵut equal on each side— neither side seems less flat than the other. On close inspection, we can see no common-sense reason why the penny should be *biased*, be more likely to come down on one side than the other. Also, there is no known scientific reason

TABLE 1

First Experiment: Tossing a Coin 50 Times

No. of Toss	Outcome	No. of Toss	Outcome	No. of Toss	Outcome
1	H	21	H	41	T
2	H	22	T	42	H
3	H	23	H	43	T
4	T	24	H	44	H
5	H	25	T	45	H
6	T	26	T	46	T
7	H	27	T	47	T
8	T	28	H	48	H
9	T	29	T	49	H
10	H	30	H	50	T
11	T	31	H		
12	H	32	T		
13	H	33	H		
14	H	34	H		
15	H	35	T		
16	T	36	H		
17	T	37	H		
18	T	38	T		
19	T	39	H		
20	T	40	H		

Result of 50 tosses: 27 heads, 23 tails

why the penny should fall on one side more often than on the other.

For the experiment, take a sheet of paper and put down the numbers 1 to 50 in a column. Then toss the penny 50 times, one after another, making sure that it turns over and over for each toss, and for each toss, record in a second column next to the first one the outcome of that toss, writing *H* for an outcome of heads and *T* for an outcome of tails. The table you make will look very much like Table 1, on facing page, which shows what actually happened when I did this experiment when writing this chapter.

Next, in your table, count up the total number of *H*'s and the total number of *T*'s. Your total will be something like the total shown in Table 1, where there are 27 heads and 23 tails.

Probability — First Approach

We are now ready to begin talking about the mathematical meaning of probability.

Based on certain experience which consists of the record of "favorable" and "unfavorable" outcomes of a certain number of repeated, similar events, we define:

(The probability of a favorable outcome of an event) IS EQUAL TO (the number of favorable outcomes) DIVIDED BY (the number of all outcomes)

For example, in the present case, based on the experience in Table 1, we have:

(The probability of obtaining heads in this experiment) IS EQUAL TO (the number of times we obtained heads, 27) DIVIDED BY (the number of all tosses, 50)

Carrying out the operation, we have:

(the probability of obtaining heads in this experiment) $= 27 \div 50$, or 0.54

If we consider all kinds of experiments and classify outcomes as favorable or unfavorable, clearly the smallest

TABLE 2

Second Experiment: Tossing a Coin 50 Times

No. of Toss	Outcome	No. of Toss	Outcome	No. of Toss	Outcome
1	T	21	H	41	H
2	H.	22	T	42	T
3	H	23	H	43	H
4	T	24	T	44	T
5	H	25	H	45	H
6	H	26	T	46	T
7	T	27	T	47	H
8	H	28	T	48	H
9	H	29	H	49	H
10	H	30	H	50	T
11	T	31	T		
12	T	32	T		
13	H	33	H		
14	H	34	T		
15	H	35	H		
16	T	36	H		
17	T	37	H		
18	H	38	H		
19	H	39	T		
20	H	40	T		

Result of 50 tosses: 29 heads, 21 tails

collection of possible favorable outcomes is NONE; and the largest collection of possible favorable outcomes is ALL; and so the probability of a favorable outcome always ranges from 0 (for impossible or never) up to 1 (for certainty or always). And a "50-50 chance" is popular language for a probability of 1/2.

Increasing the Number of Experiments

Now if the record of Table 1 were the only information available to us for judging the chance of tossing heads with a penny, we might well say (and even believe):

The probability of getting heads (0.54) is greater than

TABLE 3

Third Experiment: Tossing a Coin 50 Times

No. of Toss	Outcome	No. of Toss	Outcome	No. of Toss	Outcome
1	H	21	H	41	T
2	H	22	H	42	T
3	T	23	T	43	T
4	H	24	H	44	T
5	H	25	H	45	T
6	T	26	T	46	T
7	H	27	H	47	H
8	T	28	H	48	H
9	H	29	H	49	T
10	T	30	T	50	T
11	T	31	H		
12	T	32	H		
13	T	33	H		
14	T	34	H		
15	T	35	T		
16	H	36	H		
17	T	37	T		
18	H	38	T		
19	H	39	T		
20	H	40	T		

Result of 50 tosses: 24 heads, 26 tails

the probability of getting tails (0.46, the result of 23 divided by 50).

But it would be incorrect to believe this. First, one experiment of 50 throws is not enough in a case like this for such a judgment. Also, because of the lack of bias of an ordinary penny and our earlier judgment that the chance in the long run is 50-50, we would be disinclined to believe in 0.54 as the probability.

What happens if we increase the number of tosses?

Suppose we make another experiment of another 50 tosses. The results of this experiment are shown in Table 2 (which reports another actual experiment made some years ago).

TABLE 4

Summary Record of Experiments

No. of Heads	Experiment 1	Experiment 2	Experiment 3	Total
18				0
19				0
20				0
21				0
22				0
23				0
24			1	1
25				0
26				0
27	1			1
28				0
29		1		1
30				0
31				0
32				0

In this experiment, the resulting number of heads is 29, and the number of tails is 21. "Aha!" we might be inclined to say. "You see, there is a tendency for a penny to come down heads!"

This is a typical kind of illusion that the operation of chance sometimes fosters.

But let's go ahead and make one more experiment—the third one. The result of this is shown in Table 3: 24 heads and 26 tails. So, even with only three experiments, we have reached the point where the judgment "more chance of heads than tails" is called into question. Let us summarize our results in Table 4.

The Results of Many Experiments

What would happen if we made many, many experiments?

TABLE 5

Classification of Experiments According to the Number of Heads Recorded — Expected Distribution for 100 Experiments

No. of Heads	No. of Experiments With That No. of Heads
17	1
18	2
19	3
20	4
21	6
22	8
23	10
24	11
25	11
26	11
27	10
28	8
29	6
30	4
31	3
32	2
33	1
Correction (from rounding off)	−1
Total	100

First, we would need to take into account the time necessary to make one experiment. Suppose it took somebody working quickly (and having ready ahead of time suitable record forms) three minutes to make one experiment. Each experiment would involve 50 tosses of the coin, 50 recordings of each outcome, and two summarizing counts to report the total number of heads observed and the total number of tails observed (check total, 50).

Thus, half an hour would be needed to make ten experiments, and five hours would be needed to make 100 experiments. If the probability of tossing heads were exactly 1/2, then the expected results (calculated by mathematical

TABLE 6

**Classification of Experiments According to the Number of Heads Observed—
Expected Distribution for 1000 Experiments**

No. of Heads	No. of Experiments With That No. of Heads
14	1
15	2
16	4
17	9
18	16
19	27
20	42
21	60
22	79
23	96
24	108
25	112
26	108
27	96
28	79
29	60
30	42
31	27
32	16
33	9
34	4
35	2
36	1
Correction (from rounding off)	0
Total	1000

methods not explained here) would be as shown in Table 5. This shows that the smallest number of observed heads to be expected is 17, the largest number of observed heads to be expected is 33, and more than half the experiments (53) would have the number of heads 23, 24, 25, 26, or 27.

In one week of solid work (50 hours of experimenting), we could expect to produce one thousand experiments, and

TABLE 7

**Classification of Experiments According to the Number of Heads Observed—
Expected Distribution for 10,000 Experiments**

No. of Heads	No. of Experiments With That No. of Heads	No. of Heads	No. of Experiments With That No. of Heads
0	0	26	1080
1	0	27	960
2	0	28	788
3	0	29	596
4	0	30	419
5	0	31	270
6	0	32	160
7	0	33	87
8	0	34	44
9	0	35	20
10	0	36	8
11	0	37	3
12	1	38	1
13	3	39	0
14	8	40	0
15	20	41	0
16	44	42	0
17	87	43	0
18	160	44	0
19	270	45	0
20	419	46	0
21	596	47	0
22	788	48	0
23	960	49	0
24	1080	50	0
25	1123		

Correction (from rounding off)	+5
Total	10,000

the expected results of these experiments would be as shown in Table 6.

There would likely be one experiment (or case) with as few as 14 heads and another case with as many as 36 heads. And there would be 112 cases expected with exactly 25 heads, but there would be 108 cases expected of 24 heads and 108 cases of 26 heads.

In ten weeks of solid work of 50 hours a week, we could put together 10,000 observed cases. The expected results would be as shown in Table 7. There would be expected one case with as few heads as 12, and one case with as many heads as 38, and now there would be expected 1123 cases with 25 heads, very close to the 1080 cases of 24 heads and the 1080 cases of 26 heads.

Actually, of course, there would be some fluctuations; there would be some departure from the expected situation.

As we experimented, would we ever reach a case where all 50 throws would be heads or all 50 throws would be tails?

Almost certainly, nothing so rare would ever happen to us.

The chance of this happening, in fact, can be calculated: about once in 1,000,000,000,000,000 ($1/10^{15}$) experiments —once in a million billion experiments, each involving tossing a coin 50 times. And this is beyond the limit of practical probability. At the three-minute rate, it would require something like two billion people working eight hours every day in the year for five years to produce a million billion experiments. And we would expect just one of these experiments to be a record of 50 heads, or 50 tails, with no exceptions.

Probability — Second Approach

We are now ready to go a little further in talking about the mathematical meaning of probability.

Based on a much broader experience, we define:
(The probability of a favorable outcome of an event belonging to a certain type) IS EQUAL TO THE LIMIT OF [(the number of favorable outcomes) DIVIDED BY (the number of all outcomes)] AS (the number of all observed events belonging to this type) INCREASES WITHOUT LIMIT.

In other words, we keep on collecting events (of the type we are interested in) and we keep on observing the results of the experiments, and computing the quotient, and we keep on trying to discover (guess, estimate, or calculate) the fraction which the quotient approaches as the number of observed events of this type becomes larger and larger and larger.

How many events do you have to observe to know that the probability is exactly 1/2?

An infinite number of events! We never can observe enough instances.

The best we can do is to observe enough cases to be "very sure" that the true probability is very close to 1/2. We can specify the "degree of sureness" numerically (the statisticians call it "confidence level"). We can specify the "degree of closeness" or the amount of leeway (the statisticians call it "error" or "departure" or "deviation"). Under these conditions, we can get a mathematical answer to the expected number of cases which we must observe in order to be confident to a specified degree.

Frequency Distributions

Another powerful and important idea worthy of attention is the idea of *frequency distribution*. It has already been used a number of times in this chapter without being called by name.

For example, the report of Experiment 1, "27 heads and 23 tails out of 50 tosses," is a "distribution of the frequency" of 50 throws into the two classes, heads and tails. For another example, in the report of the expected results of 100 theoretical experiments in Table 5, we showed a "frequency distribution." In this table, the number 11 written opposite the number of heads, 25, is the expected number or count or "frequency" of experiments with 25 heads observed.

Often the reporting of how probability or chance operates in a situation is most usefully summed up in a "frequency

distribution": a table showing how the total number of observations (the "total frequency") is classified (or "distributed") among the various classes or classifications.

A famous kind of frequency distribution has the name
"normal distribution." It has many observations clustering
around the middle, and fewer and fewer observations toward
the sides. The distribution of Table 7 is very much like a
normal distribution.

Another kind of frequency distribution has the name
"uniform distribution." In such a distribution, each observation is equally likely to fall anywhere. A good example is the
distribution of digits in the four-digit part of telephone numbers. If we had one hundred telephone numbers of four
digits, we would expect that the digits 0, 1, 2, 3, 4, 5, 6, 7, 8, 9
would each occur about equally often (about 40 times) —
with no reason to expect any digit, such as 8, to occur systematically more often than any other digit, such as 4.

In fact, why not make the experiment, and take a look?

In Table 8 (facing page) appears a list of one hundred
such telephone numbers. (The source was page 331, column
4 of the Manhattan (N.Y.) telephone directory for 1958-59.)
These are telephone numbers for *ordinary* subscribers, excluding those cases where a hospital, college, or other large
organization has a number of listings all with the same
telephone number.

Tallying the digits and summarizing the tallies, we obtain columns (1) and (2) of Table 9. Looking over the observed frequencies in column (2), we notice the departures
from 40, which is the expected number of occurrences of
each kind of digit 0 to 9. We notice that not one of the observed frequencies is 40, and that they range from a low of
32 to a high of 50. In other words, the departures range from
eight below the expected frequency of 40 to ten above it.
Is this pattern of departures reasonable or unreasonable?
Are the departures significant?

TABLE 8   100 Telephone Numbers Taken at Random

1872	7445	9174	5838	2683
8487	4868	0985	8109	2861
8248	0499	0050	9460	5985
5697	0639	5565	8797	4356
4818	6144	0442	8106	1688
8492	6061	2495	3332	1518
2006	7706	5786	8983	4610
6219	8430	9397	2795	1619
3440	4459	9460	3332	1305
5790	7976	2060	3070	0228
3747	9017	1487	8409	3285
2422	8177	5764	4948	9616
4292	1550	7786	3131	6126
2114	6711	2800	5840	8675
1897	9754	5605	6485	5906
7800	0517	7334	3794	8372
2067	3064	5312	5797	4841
0397	3326	1775	4767	2207
3496	0270	6485	6875	8460
5467	7179	0471	1131	6327

TABLE 9   Frequency Distribution of Digits in 100 Telephone Numbers

Digit (1)	Observed Frequency (2)	Expected Frequency (3)	Observed Probability $(2) \div 400 =$ (4)	Expected Probability $(3) \div 400 =$ (5)
0	44	40	.110	.100
1	38	40	.095	.100
2	32	40	.080	.100
3	32	40	.080	.100
4	46	40	.115	.100
5	36	40	.090	.100
6	43	40	.108	.100
7	50	40	.125	.100
8	44	40	.110	.100
9	35	40	.088	.100
Correction for Rounding			−.001	0
Total	400	400	1.000	1.000

There is a good statistical test that can be applied to answer this question. It is called the Chi-Square Test; we shall not explain it here, but simply use it. Applying the test, the answer is that the departures are "not significant"; in fact, the test in this case tells us that in about one out of three experiments we would expect to get a distribution more divergent from the expected frequency of 40 than this.

Bias

We shall finish this discussion of probability and frequency distributions by commenting on two widespread conditions.

One of these conditions is the effect of bias, the distortion produced by choosing or selecting after events have occurred. For example, in tossing a penny, if a person notices chiefly those cases where heads turn up, and notices hardly at all the cases where tails turn up, the experiments rapidly show a lasting predominance of heads.

Or suppose a person classifies days into two kinds: lucky days and unlucky days—and he decides a day is lucky only by what happens on that day. Immediately, bias, distortion, falsity, creep into his statistics on the outcomes of days. The necessary conditions for random probability to operate no longer exist.

I once knew a lovely, optimistic lady, much older than I, who often took the subway with me in New York. Once she said to me, "Look how my mental power affects the trains — they always stop with the doors opening in front of me!" Well, as I traveled with her in the subway, I proceeded to point out to her the many times when the trains stopped with the doors opened not in front of her but some distance away. But she was just annoyed with me for pointing out the contrary instances. She seemed unable to listen when I tried to explain that the ratio of door space to the total length of a subway car was about 40 percent, making the expected probability that the doors would open in front of her equal to about four out of ten times.

Repeatability

Besides bias as a hazard to judgment about chances, there is also a more profound problem: the difficulty in the real world of actually repeating certain kinds of events. In the artificial world of experimenting, such as in tossing a coin, or testing rats in a maze, it is easy for the experimenter to:

- isolate the event,
- control all conditions, and
- repeat the event each time in what seems to be almost exactly the same way.

Even the genetic stock of the rats can be closely controlled for purposes of experiment. But in the real world, repeatability is not so easy.

For example, in the test planting of new strains of hybrid corn, how can we be sure that the experimental plantings are all treated alike? Some of the plots may be in a lower part of the field; some may be at the edge instead of in the middle; some may be slightly better fertilized than others; some may be weeded just before a rain, others may be weeded just after a rain; and so forth. And, of course, every grain of seed corn is genetically a little bit different from every other grain.

The statisticians are able to supply good advice on how to control the size, position, and treatment of the experimental plots. They are also able to advise how much of the variation observed between plots is very likely to be meaningful and how much of the variation is very likely to be attributable to chance fluctuation. In this way, repeatability is approached.

But, in many instances in the real world, we may know perfectly well that we can never repeat a particular event. It might, for example, be the marriage of Michelle Taine and

John Scott. Someone may say, "I think it will probably wind up in divorce—they are too unlike, and they come from different nationalities." But it is utterly impossible to make once more the "experiment" of their marriage under the same conditions in the real world: this kind of event can happen only once. If indeed it should happen a second time —sometimes two persons who have divorced each other marry each other once more—then they have surely substantially changed by that time.

There seems to be no good way of applying mathematical probability to happenings in the real world that are one of a kind. The word "probably" has in these cases a kind of unclear, indefinite, and very human meaning, such as that possessed by "ever so much" in the utterance "I love you ever so much."

Part Four

MATHEMATICS
AND THE ENVIRONMENT

Going from Ordinary Language into Mathematics

18

How to Translate from Ordinary Language into Mathematics

In order to make the ideas of mathematics do useful work for us, we need to learn the techniques of mathematics. For example, in arithmetic, we need to learn the technique to be used in adding 8796 to 3425, even if we have nothing real around us to which those numbers apply.

But in addition to learning techniques expressed in mathematical language, we also need to learn something more; and that is how to translate from ordinary language (and ordinary situations) into mathematical language. Otherwise we cannot apply the mathematical techniques to situations. In other words, we have to learn how to pass from the ordinary everyday, complex, changing world that we perceive around us, with its multitudinous, scintillating facets, into the simple bare mathematical language needed for expressing the essence of a problem.

To give practice in such translating is the purpose of what are called "word problems" in many mathematics textbooks.

Translating by Human Beings into Arithmetical Language

Most of us get a good deal of practice in one area of translation into mathematical language: translating into the

253

language of arithmetic. One Christmas Eve, I asked my small granddaughter, "How old are you, Charlene?" Charlene smiled and said "Six"; but her mother promptly spoke up and said "No, Charlene, you are three, three years old!" Charlene was in the process of learning how to translate from her ordinary everyday world into the language of arithmetic.

In regard to arithmetic, a great many of us learn rather well at an early age how to go from our ordinary world into the language of arithmetic. Gaining this habit effectively is one of the remarkable accomplishments of human beings. Although crows, for example, can count to four, no other animal comes anywhere near the accomplishment of the human being in counting or adding.

In the same way, before we can apply other parts of mathematics, we must become used to the ideas that occur in these other parts of mathematics and we must develop the ability to recognize their indications in the real world.

Translating by Machines into Mathematical Language

The power to observe parts of the real world and convert these observations into mathematical language, language which can be computed with, is not limited to animals. On the contrary, a great variety of machines and instruments have been constructed to make observations of the real world, either at the command of human beings or independently; and they produce quantities of information that can be calculated with, and the results are used to control processes or other situations.

When an oil refinery is operating, instruments installed here and there in the system of pipes and tanks record such physical variables as:

- temperature
- pressure
- viscosity

- speed of flow
- liquid level (if the container contains liquid)

and many more.

In testing the scale model of a proposed airplane in a wind tunnel, instruments are connected by wires or in other ways to various parts of the model, and "strain gauges" record the amount of strain as air currents of various speeds flow past the stationary model.

Electronic counting devices may "record" the flow of traffic over a highway, or they may "watch" the falling of pills into a medicine bottle and cause a mechanism to stop the flow exactly as the hundredth pill falls into the bottle.

All these instrument readings may be fed directly into modern computers; then the computer, according to a program of instructions, solves the processing problem and calculates the changes that appear to be desirable. Or the instrument readings may be fed, directly or almost directly, into valves, latches, gates, hoppers, and other acting mechanisms, to control their operation.

The Translation of a Problem —
Disregarding Irrelevant Information

Let us take a look at what happens when we go from the words of a problem in ordinary language to the words that express the mathematical ideas quite precisely.

VERSION 1

John Jones is a track coach; he regularly carries a stopwatch in his pocket. While he is on a summer holiday in New Hampshire, he notices a farmer chopping down a dead pine tree some distance away across a meadow. A number of times Jones sees the farmer strike the tree trunk with the ax and then a little bit later he hears the sound of the ax stroke. Taking out his stopwatch and measuring, he decides that the time between seeing the ax stroke and hearing its sound is just about 3/5 of a second. How far away is the farmer?

The question in this problem is "How far away?" So the answer will be a distance. Distance in this case implies two locations, the location of the event (the ax stroke) and the location of the observer (John Jones).

A great deal of the other information given in the problem makes no difference at all, is irrelevant, such as:
- the geographic area (New Hampshire)
- the name of the person watching (John Jones)
- why he happened to be watching (summer holiday)
- the occupation of the person chopping (farmer)
- the nature of the tree being chopped (dead pine tree)
- what occupies the intervening distance (a meadow)
- the cause of the sound (the ax)

and much more. All this other information is irrelevant, or seems to be.

How do we know which information is irrelevant? In many cases we know because of our experience, our education, and our knowledge of science. In some cases we do not know until further investigation and experiment. There are no completely general rules for telling what is relevant and what is irrelevant. In fact, a lot of human progress, it seems, consists of noticing some factor previously thought irrelevant, discovering that it *is* relevant, and controlling it.

Let us leave out the information that appears to be irrelevant and rephrase the problem, seeking to express its essence:

VERSION 2

An observer sees an event, and about 3/5 of a second later hears it. How far apart are the observer and the event?

This version represents a great deal of progress toward mathematical language and a mathematical solution. The answer to the problem in this version will be the answer to the problem in the first version.

Additional Needed Data and Assumptions

But what do we do now?

First, we consider the speed of "seeing" by means of light. We look in a physics book or book of formulas to find out how fast light travels. We find that light travels at about 186,000 miles a second; so, because of the short distance away that the observer must be from the event, we can treat the seeing as instantaneous. In other words, we disregard the time that it takes for the light reflected from the ax stroke to reach the eyes of the track coach.

Second, we consider the speed of "hearing" by means of sound. We look up the speed of sound. This turns out to be 1088 feet per second, and the physics book adds:

"in air, at sea-level altitude, and 32 degrees Fahrenheit temperature."

Neither version of the problem says anything about the temperature of the day, or the altitude above sea level of the meadow. So let's try to keep things simple for ourselves; let's assume that it's a cold day, even if summer, and that the meadow is lowland, not far from the seacoast (New Hampshire has a seacoast—aha!, irrelevant factor becoming slightly relevant!).

Third, let's consider the reported 3/5 of a second. The finest subdivisions of time that an ordinary stopwatch can measure is fifths of a second; this is close to the limits of human accuracy in observing times. Who did the observing? John Jones, track coach. Well, he certainly would have had experience timing events with a stopwatch; so let's assume that he measured the time, of 3/5 of a second, fairly accurately; in fact, he might have measured it several times in order to be certain, and averaged his measurements. (More factors in the original version of the problem are therefore

258 | *Mathematics and the Environment*

becoming slightly relevant.) So we are now ready for a third
version rephrasing the problem once more:

VERSION 3

An observer sees an event, and 3/5 of a second
later hears it. Assume: hearing through air; altitude
at sea level; and competent measuring of the fraction of the second to within, say, 10 percent.

How far apart are the observer and the event? We can
use the formula: (speed) × (time) = (distance). The answer
to this version of the problem is to be accepted as the answer
to the first version—even though, when we apply the assumptions, the problem has changed a little.

Here again is a technique often used in dealing with
problems as they arise in the real world, since they come
without sufficient data. We make some reasonable assumptions, solve the resulting problem, and accept that answer
(with some caution) as representing the answer to the
original problem.

The Calculation

Now we can apply an arithmetical formula to finding the
distance:

(speed) MULTIPLIED BY (time) EQUALS (distance)

1088 feet per second × 3/5 of a second = 653 feet

Ten percent is 65 feet, more or less. So the true distance is
probably somewhere between 600 and 700 feet. This is
about an eighth of a mile, since a mile is 5280 feet.

Answer: About an eighth of a mile.

To verify the answer, we divide 653 feet by 1080 feet
per second, and come out with 3/5 of a second, which checks.

We can observe here something which is quite common:
the arithmetical calculation by itself was much simpler than
the process of translating the problem from ordinary lan-

guage into mathematical ideas, changing from one version of the problem to another, and finding the data to calculate with.

The General Process

In the preceding example we see a good illustration of the process that is applied over and over in going from ordinary language into mathematical language:

1) Consider each of the factors mentioned in the problem.
2) Decide which are relevant and which are irrelevant.
3) Disregard the irrelevant factors.
4) Rephrase the problem expressing its essence.
5) Look up information or data that bears on the essential problem.
6) Make reasonable assumptions, if necessary.
7) Rephrase the problem for the third time, using all the relevant data and stating as clearly as possible the assumptions and mathematical relations.
8) Calculate the answer.
9) Put the answer back into the conditions of the original problem, and test the answer with these questions: Does it satisfy the conditions? Is it reasonable? Does it make sense?

Kinds of Problems — and Mathematics

19

ANOTHER PART of the appreciation and understanding of mathematics comes from knowing something about the kinds and classifications of problems from the point of view of mathematics and the real world.

For example, take the problem:

How much is three fifths of four ninths?

Of course we think first of classifying a mathematical problem according to the branch of mathematics that is needed to solve it. We may say:

> Oh, that is a problem in arithmetic — there is an "of" and "of" means "multiply," and you have to multiply to solve that problem.

Although this remark is true for this problem, unfortunately there are many problems where the word "of" is not a signal for the operation "multiply."

Even if we can tell for some problems that they are problems in arithmetic, there are many problems that you and I will not know at first glance how to classify; it may not be easy to determine what branch of mathematics to apply to solve them. And some problems may require more than one branch of mathematics for their solution. So this particular scheme for classifying problems, though natural to all who have had any training in arithmetic, algebra, and geometry, is not a classification scheme that a nonmathematician can readily apply.

260

There are some very important classifications of problems which we as intelligent nonmathematicians can apply — and often do apply—to problems that we encounter in the real world. Such problems often are either clearly mathematical or have some mathematical fringe. Following are some of these classifications:

Reality or fiction. The problem is real or not real.

Usefulness. The answer (if we find it out) is useful or not useful.

Data. The problem comes with data or without data.

Number of answers. There are many answers, just one answer, or no answer.

Approximate answers. The problem has approximate answers or not.

Technique for solving. The method of solving requires a simple technique or an advanced technique.

Let us take a look at each of these classifications.

Real Problems and Unreal Problems

A *real* problem is a problem that relates to the real world and deals with conditions and numbers that could actually occur or apply. Here are some examples:

- What rate of interest should money earn if it is to double in 15 years?
- How large a group of people all of the same age at last birthday need to be observed for a year in order to be almost certain that their annual death rate is between $8\frac{1}{2}$ and $9\frac{1}{2}$ per thousand?

These are real problems. First, they deal with conditions that occur in the real world. Second, the numbers that occur in them are numbers that are appropriate in the real world. For example, suppose we should ask:

What rate of interest should money earn if it is to double in two years?

This would be an unreal problem, for nowhere in the ordinary real world is there obtainable a rate of interest by means of which money would double in two years.

An *unreal* problem does not relate to the real world or else it includes conditions or numbers contrary to fact or possibility. Such a problem may of course be interesting and worth solving for other reasons; yet, from the point of view of a busy man interested in problems that could actually occur in the real world, an unreal problem seems a silly waste of time and effort. (In some cases, it may actually be a wise use of time and effort — but will still appear silly; some instances are mentioned below.)

For another example, there is the famous medieval scholastic problem:

How many angels can dance on the point of a needle? In the real world there exist no angels; no one can reasonably say how big an angel is. And so the problem is unreal.

Another example is:

If six apples cost five cents, how much will 12 apples cost?

Apples no longer cost less than a cent apiece. And if a classroom teacher asks this question, some student is likely to respond, "You can't buy six apples for five cents!"

Finally:

Is it true that 6 is the 3173rd digit in the decimal fraction expressing pi? Pi (π, 3.14159265 . . .) is the ratio of the circumference of a circle to its diameter; for example, the fifth digit in the decimal fraction is 9.

This problem is unreal, because the greatest accuracy of pi needed for the largest physically existing circle known is far less than 3000 decimal digits of decimal fraction. In fact, suppose we imagine a circle with a diameter of 12 billion light-years (the farthest distance that the 200-inch telescope at Palomar, California, can see into the depths of space is 6 billion light-years). Suppose we wanted to know the circumference of this circle accurate to the diameter of an atomic nucleus. Then we would still need fewer than 150 digits of the decimal fraction of pi.

It happens that the answer to this unreal problem is known, because an automatic electronic computer has calculated that the 3173rd digit is not 6 but 8.

But people must pay some attention to unreal problems. In the first place, the explanations for the results of new research and experiments may require the use of branches of mathematics that previously had no application in the real world. This has occurred several times. Albert Einstein, in the years before 1917 when he was working out the theory of relativity, drew on sections of mathematics which had never previously been applied: branches of geometry called non-Euclidean and mathematical entities called Lorentz transformations. Again, in the 1950's, many scientists designing circuits for computing machines drew on a kind of algebra called Boolean algebra, which had been worked out more than 50 years earlier without any application in mind to circuits for switching. And there are a number of other important and interesting examples.

In addition, for learning mathematics, simple problems with easy numbers need to be presented, so that the methods of solving these problems can be more easily understood and learned. Unfortunately, so many simple problems occur in most exercises in mathematics textbooks that a student often gathers the false impression that the real world will be as easy to deal with as the problems in his textbooks.

The Answer (If We Find It) Is Useful or Not Useful

The second scheme of classification is whether the answer to the problem is useful or not. It might be thought at first that the distinction "useful or not useful" would be almost the same as "real or unreal." In other words, if a problem is a real problem, its answer is useful, and if a problem is not real, its answer is not useful. But this is not true.

Here is a problem which is not real, but its answer is useful:

> Using straightedge and compasses only, construct a square exactly equal in area to the area of a given circle.

This famous problem is called "Squaring the Circle." It is a problem which is not real because an exact square and an exact circle are not possible in the real world. The ancient Greeks worked a good deal on this problem; from time to time since antiquity, a great many other people have tried to solve it. Approximate constructions are readily possible. But the problem was finally disposed of in the 1870's, by a rigorous proof that the construction was impossible. This answer to the problem is certainly useful: sensible people no longer spend time and energy trying to solve it, and the proof of impossibility has directed the minds of mathematicians toward other more fruitful problems.

It is very easy to construct a problem which is real but whose answer is not useful. Here is one:

> In a certain anthill there are 12,037 ants; each has six legs and two antennae; what is the total number of ant legs and antennae?

Problems with Data, and Problems without

Another important scheme of classification of mathematical problems is according to the amount of data which they come with.

> How much is three fifths of four ninths?

This problem is complete; all the data we need to answer that problem is presented in its statement.

> What is the value of a college education?

This problem contains practically no data; all it contains really is a focus, a curiosity, to which our attention is directed.

In order to answer such a problem, the first thing we need to do is to make some reasonable assumptions, such as:

1) Consider a typical student graduating from college, say, at age 22, and compare him with a typical student not going to college graduating from high school at 18.

2) Assume a probable working lifetime up to a fairly common age when people retire—say, age 65.

3) Estimate the income which a typical college graduate earns year by year, and compare it with the income which a typical high school graduate earns year by year. To find out these income figures we either draw on our knowledge and experience of the ordinary everyday world or else we look up appropriate statistics in an almanac or government reference source.

With these assumptions made, the problem has a reasonable answer.

The problems that usually appear in ordinary mathematics textbooks come with their data. There seems to be general agreement among textbook writers to put into each problem a sufficient capsule of data so that the problem can be solved. This has the added advantage that the textbook author can supply an answer, and it is the "right" answer. But this style of selecting problems does not give a good impression of the real world, which is a very untidy world, where problems almost never appear with just the suitable capsule of data.

The usual problem in the real world appears without data, without the information and figures on the basis of which you or I can calculate an answer. Instead, the problem usually begins with a chunk of curiosity in one's mind:

> Ha, there's the Jones's new car! I wonder how he can afford it?

And a mathematically inclined friend says to you:

> "Let's estimate."

He makes a list of points about Mr. Jones: his house, his car, his vacations, and other indications of his wealth or lack of it. Finally he has enough information listed so that you and he can estimate how much Mr. Jones earns in the course of a year.

Since the usual way in which problems arise in the real world is without data, you need to work to get appropriate data. Often this is more work and takes longer than doing the calculating.

The Number of Answers

Another way of classifying mathematical problems is according to the number of answers. Problems may have many answers, just one answer, or no answer.

Here again, the run of problems in the ordinary mathematics textbook gives a completely misleading impression. The characteristic problem in the ordinary textbook has a single answer. This is nice for the student, because when he finds the one answer he can stop working, and nice for the teacher, because when he examines the single answer, he knows a lot about how the student has done.

But problems that come up in the real world, and for which you and I have to gather the data, more usually have many answers—or no answers. Problems with a single answer are rare.

> How shall I live on an income of $100 a week, dividing it among my expenses?

In the United States in the 1960's this is a reasonable income for a single person, and there are literally thousands of answers to the problem, as the income is distributed among food, shelter, clothing, travel, entertainment, repairs, taxes, etc.

> How will 84 million people be fully employed in 75 million jobs?

The answer is "It's impossible." And retraining, reeducation, etc., simply change the identity of the persons who are holding the jobs.

It is worth being alert to the number of answers to a problem. Many of the fallacies committed by people in their daily reasoning are linked with failure to realize that there may be many solutions to a problem, or no solutions.

Approximate Answers

One of the sources of more than one answer to a problem is degree of accuracy or approximation. A problem may have one accurate answer and a number of different approximate answers. For example, one third may be expressed decimally as 33 percent. But three thirds is equal to one, whereas three times 33 percent is equal to 99 percent, and this is not the same as 100 percent. To get around this obstacle, we usually say that 1/3 is 33.33 percent on two occasions and 33.34 percent on the third occasion. Even this may not be accurate enough in some cases.

As a rule, if you are calculating a set of percentages that ought to add to 100.00 percent, you add up the column of percents and see if the result is 99.98 percent or 99.99 percent or 100.01 percent or 100.02 percent. If so, you assume that *rounding-off errors*, as they are called, have occurred, and you arbitrarily change by .01 the one or two largest percents in the column in such a way that the total of the percents is forced to be 100.00 percent.

From the philosophical point of view, we can confidently decide that the real world is full of only approximate answers to problems. For example, in mathematics, a line can be divided indefinitely—there is no limit to the accuracy with which we can separate two parts of a line. Thus, in mathematics, on a line from 0 to 3, the mark for the square root of two, 1.41428 . . . , makes an extraordinary cut. At this cut, all fractions can be divided sharply into those which are less than the square root of two and those that are more.

But in the real world there are no corresponding physical operations. In regard to any line three units long that we may draw in any room on earth, we cannot even be as accurate in dividing it as 20 decimal places.

So, in essence, much of mathematics concerns ideal or imagined concepts, which have an interesting and important, but basically approximate, relation to what exists in the real world.

And this means that whenever we go from mathematics to the real world, we must pick up a spoonful of caution, a pinch of salt, and apply our mathematical results a bit questioningly.

The Technique for Getting an Answer

Finally, problems may be divided into those needing a lot of mathematical technique, and those needing only a little.

> Where and when will the next total eclipse of the sun
> by the moon be visible on the earth?

This is a problem requiring a good deal of mathematical technique — and a rough answer is useless to someone who wants to observe the next total eclipse.

Even though I have studied mathematics for more than 45 years, including subjects such as calculus, differential equations, and functions of a complex variable, I am sure it would take me at least a couple of weeks, using only my own resources, to calculate the answer to this problem. I would need to look up references for records of the positions of the sun, moon, and earth; I would have to look for formulas predicting eclipses; I would have to study the mathematics of how to apply them. To solve this problem would require from me more work, studying, and time than I could easily afford; and I would ordinarily leave this problem for a professional mathematician or astronomer.

But there are many, many problems for which the technique for getting a good answer is very simple. Perhaps one multiplication, or a couple of divisions, or adding a few numbers, or reasoning about the various possible cases will quickly lead to an acceptable or correct answer.

How far can I drive on a full tank of gas if my car goes $15\frac{1}{2}$ miles on a gallon? Only one multiplication is needed for this problem: (number of gallons in the full tank) MULTIPLIED BY $15\frac{1}{2}$ EQUALS (the answer).

> I have a nickel, a quarter, and a 50-cent piece in my pocket. How many differently priced articles can I buy, using one or more of these coins and receiving no change?

For this problem we have to count cases. If we use one coin only, we can pay five cents, or 25 cents, or 50 cents, and this makes three kinds. If we use two coins only, we can pay 30 cents, or 55 cents, or 75 cents; this makes the total number of kinds six. If we use all three coins, we can pay 80 cents. The total number of kinds is seven; that exhausts the possibilities. So our answer is seven.

Gradually, as we become more and more experienced and educated, we absorb many of the simpler techniques of mathematics, and become able to use them well in order to get answers to problems.

Computers and Mathematics

ANOTHER INFLUENCE affecting the intelligent nonmathematician which is intimately related to mathematics is the tidal upsurge of automatic computers, or "electronic brains" as many people irreverently name them.

The Growth of Computers

In 1944 the first of the automatic digital computers (known as the Harvard IBM Automatic Sequence-Controlled Calculator) was finished. It went to work in the basement of the physics laboratory at Harvard University, Cambridge, Massachusetts. It had been designed as a joint project by Professor Howard H. Aiken of Harvard and International Business Machines Corporation. It handled numbers of 23 decimal digits with a fixed decimal point; it could remember 72 of them at one time and refer to any one of them in 3/10 of a second; it performed an addition in 3/10 of a second and a multiplication in four seconds. It could not handle alphabetic characters.

By 1965, 20 years later, more than 30,000 automatic computers were at work all over the world, with over 20,000 of them in use in the United States. One of the most powerful computers, called LARC (made by Sperry Rand Corporation), handled numbers of 12 decimal digits with what is called a "floating" decimal point. It could remember 100,000 of these numbers at one time, and could recall any one of them in four microseconds (millionths of a second); it performed addition in four microseconds and multiplication in eight microseconds. It handled alphabetic characters also. Later machines are even faster and more powerful.

The Applications of Computers

Automatic computers are solving problems and answering questions on a scale so vast that it is hard to imagine. In 20 years, human society has added to its productive capital equipment computing power in excess of 150 million reasoning operations per second.

A large part of this computing power is devoted to scientific, engineering, and military problems, but another very large part is devoted to problems of business, industry, and government. An inventory of the kinds of applications, made by the magazine *Computers and Automation* in June 1965, showed over 800 distinct areas of application of computers. Here are a few examples (excluding scientific and engineering):

Warehousing and stocking: records, analysis
Production: routing cable and electrical wiring
Advertising: analysis of consumer audiences
Banking: signature verification
Hospital laboratory experiments: automatic control
Stock market: price indexes computed hourly
Life insurance: nonforfeiture value calculations
Law: crime analysis, prediction, and detection
Oil field analysis: correlation of data from different drill holes
Oil refineries: simulation
Sports: scoring of Olympic games
Building construction: scheduling
Textiles: fabric quality control
Parking garages: automatic control

What Is a Computer?

An automatic computer is a machine that performs reasonable operations on information, transfers information automatically from one part of the machine to another, and has a flexible control over the sequence of operations.

There are basically three kinds of computers:

- Digital computers, which handle information in the form of numbers made up of *digits* and words made up of letters;
- Analog computers, which handle information in the form of magnitudes of physical variables such as electrical voltage or the amount of turning of a shaft, which are *analogous* to the mathematical variables in the problem;
- Hybrid computers, which, like a human being, are in some parts of their structure digital and in other parts of their structure analog.

The great majority of automatic computers at the present time consists of digital computers: they are versatile; they are accurate beyond the power of physical measurements to be accurate; they are very fast; and they are exceedingly reliable. An important proportion, however, of all computers is analog—there are problems for which an analog computer is unsurpassed. Hybrid computers are still new, and not much can yet be said about them.

The Simplicity of Computers

One of the extraordinary facts about computers is that they are basically and conceptually remarkably simple.

Every automatic digital computer is much more simple basically than, say, an automobile. A digital computer is essentially made up of five parts:

- *Input,* where numbers and other data go into the machine — as, for example, the keyboard of an adding machine whereby numbers are entered into it;
- *Output,* where numbers and other data come out of the machine, as, for example, the paper tape in an ordinary adding machine where numbers are put out in the form of printed characters on paper;
- The *processor* or calculating unit or arithmetic unit, where information is processed, i.e., numbers are added, words are compared, etc.;
- *Memory* or storage, where numbers or words are held unchanged in "boxes" or "cells" (registers) from one time to a later time;
- The *control unit,* which controls the sequence of reasonable operations to be carried out by the machine, usually by executing a program (a set of instructions) stored in the memory of the machine, expressed in the form of a long sequence of very simple commands.

The structure of a digital computer is something like what a railroad would be if *1)* freight cars loaded with information were able to be sent here and there anywhere (as specified) at the speed of light, and *2)* in addition to the railroad line and stations, there were a large warehouse to store freight cars of information and a fast factory to process them.

An analog computer is organized in a different way. Each of the numbers that come into an analog computer is stored or registered in a separate mechanism, and the mechanisms are all connected in such a way that as one of them changes (representing usually the change in time), all the others change appropriately. For example, in an automobile speedometer, as a wheel of the automobile turns along the road, a sensing device next to it responds to the speed of its turning. This device transmits a proportional turning force to a flexible cable. The cable runs right into the center of the dial in the dashboard of the car, and causes the needle of the speedometer to change its position and point to a number on the dial that reports the speed of the car. A big analog computer, of course, is much more complicated; it may contain mechanisms to keep track of 200 physical variables at once, instead of just one.

What Is Information?

What we have said above depends on the meaning of two important ideas: "information" and "reasonable operation." A computer works with information; the types of operations it performs are reasonable operations. Let us clarify these ideas.

Information, from the point of view of our use of it as human beings, is likely to be thought of as one or more statements of facts, such as "The height of Mt. Everest is 29,000 feet." In other words, information is what you find in a dictionary, textbook, or almanac—and hardly at all what you find in a novel, story, or fairy tale.

Information, from the point of view of use in a computer, is something different. It is a set of marks, signs, or signals that have meaning. These marks for a digital computer are regularly digits, letters, typewriter symbols, etc.

A computer responds meaningfully to different letters and digits. It can react to the digit 4 by doing an operation four times. It can react to an occurrence of the letter k (the character for, say, the code 10010) by determining that it may be exactly equivalent to a previous occurrence of the letter k (having the same code). Other machines also deal with information, such as television or a printing press; but they do not react to the meaning of the information which they are handling.

Physically, the information in a machine is a choice of arrangements of some physical equipment. For example, one way of storing information so that a computer can refer to it is as a series of rows on paper tape, each row consisting of a pattern of holes and no-holes expressing codes; the holes correspond to 1 in the code, and the no-holes correspond to 0. So the code 10010 could be stored by the pattern: hole, no-hole, no-hole, hole, no-hole. Another way of storing information in a computer is as polarized spots on a magnetic surface. The arrangement of polarized magnetic spots— north-south, south-north, south-north, north-south, south-north—might well stand for the code 10010.

The aspect of meaning that a computer can be said to understand is the aspect of logical and mathematical consistency among the information, instructions, and operations it deals with. The computer has no knowledge, of course, of the meaning of a *k* or a 4 as it may occur in many situations in human society.

What Are Reasonable Operations?

The other idea that needs to be clarified in order to understand an automatic computer is "reasonable operations" upon information. These are mathematical and logical operations. Mathematical operations include addition, subtraction, multiplication, division, taking a square root, integrating, raising to a power, and many more. Logical operations include comparing, selecting, matching, sorting, etc., and operations of the algebra of logic (or Boolean algebra), such as AND, OR, NOT, EXCEPT, etc. Logical operations can be performed on numbers or on expressions made out of any characters including ordinary words.

By skillfully assembling these operations in various sequences, *programmers*, or persons who program computers, have achieved very remarkable sequences of reasonable operations. Among the kinds of programs which have run successfully on computers are passable translation from Russian to English, playing championship checkers, and determining which procedures to apply to what kinds of persons who have not paid their bills.

A particularly important logical operation performed by a computer is determining at some time in the course of a calculation which of two instructions called for should next be executed. The programmed computer makes this choice in the right way at the right time, because rules for choosing have been stored in its program; it consults the rules and applies them. This is called a *branching operation.*

The Relation of Computers to Mathematics

Computers have already produced profound effects on mathematics, and will in the future produce more.

First, enormous quantities of monotonous mathematical drudgery have been taken over by computers. This has freed mathematicians to do more thoughtful and interesting work.

Second, calculations which in the old days would never have been attempted are now made as a matter of routine. The successful launching and guidance of a spaceship would have been impossible without automatic computers. And there are many more achievements.

Among future possibilities that we can see are some which will be open to us when we know better how to instruct computers to work for us. Among the possibilities are these:

- Mathematicians should be able to prove many theorems whose proof is out of reach now.
- Computers should be able to apply the test of many actual trials to many conjectures in mathematics.
- Computers should be able to assist mathematicians in the manipulation of unwieldy symbolic expressions.
- We should be able to program a computer to give exceedingly good mathematical explanations and instruction—explaining certain kinds of subjects better than almost all teachers of mathematics.

The Relation of Computers to Nonmathematicians

In the course of human history there have been some great changes in the behavior of ordinary human beings towards ideas. In the years when Arabic numerals were replacing Roman numerals, many persons must have claimed that they could never get used to Arabic numerals, and they undoubtedly insisted loudly that they would never use them.

Similarly, for many years in the 1800's, computers were laughed at, scorned, and considered impossible.

The idea of an automatic machine that would add, subtract, multiply, divide, and perform a sequence of mathematical steps automatically was probably first conceived in 1822 by Charles Babbage, a professor of mathematics at Cambridge University, England. He set out to build one, worked at it for more than 20 years, and received considerable help. But after those years of effort, aid from the British Government was withdrawn because of his failure to build a useful machine. Babbage tried for many more years to carry out his ideas, but never succeeded. His failure, we can now see, was due essentially to the lack of sufficiently accurate machine tools, and lack of the mechanical and electrical devices that finally became available around 1900 to 1910. But his writings demonstrate the completeness and perfection of his concepts of an automatic computer. The people who laughed and scorned were wrong.

Computers are becoming more and more available. Therefore, if previously we were bored by tiresome drudgery in mathematics, like adding many numbers each of many digits, now we can refer this drudgery to the machine. If previously you or I could find little that was interesting in mathematics, now we are likely to be able to find much more that is interesting, because the machine makes a specialty of taking over and doing what is not interesting. If previously you or I bore the responsibility of doing our calculations correctly, now there is the promise that we will find a small electronic slave. In return for our learning how to give it instructions, it will take the responsibility of calculating correctly for us. In fact, we shall quite likely be able to buy instruction tapes that will tell this electronic slave how to solve the commonest kinds of problems we want it to solve.

The computer revolution will produce a vast change in the behavior of human beings. Great numbers of people who take Arabic numerals in their stride today will be taking computers in their stride tomorrow.

Just as millions of American boys grow up knowing a lot about the insides of automobiles, so millions of American boys and girls will soon grow up knowing a lot about the insides of computers. Just as the "driver" of an automobile is a common everyday word, so the "programmer" of a computer will become a common everyday word. Just as there is a thrill of success when a young person learns how to drive a car, so there will be another thrill of success when he learns how to give instructions to a computer so that it will solve his own problems.

An automobile has a minimum size and corresponding cost—it must be large enough to transport at least one human being. But a computer, potentially, has hardly any minimum size and cost: all it has to move around are 1's and 0's, whose representation can be microscopic. As time passes, the size of computers goes down and down, and their powers go up and up.

Just as the number of car drivers in our society is in the millions, so the number of persons who program computers is likely to rise to the millions. And any person who programs a computer—and whose program runs—is likely to have stopped being a nonmathematician!

The "New Math" and Mathematical Education

21

The "New Math" - What Is Some of the New Math? - The Concepts
Included in the New Math - Evaluation of the New Math - Basic
Principles of Teaching School Mathematics - Correctness

The "New Math"

In the summer of 1955 a commission appointed by the
College Entrance Examination Board came together to discuss the revision of mathematics teaching in the high schools
of the United States. Many people believed that the usual
courses and usual sequence of topics studied had been
frozen for far too many years. Important developments and
discoveries in mathematics during the past 200 years had
had almost no influence on the teaching of mathematics in
schools. What were recent developments in mathematics
that were interesting and important, and that should be
taught? Why not devote less time in school to topics of trivial
or doubtful value?

As a result of this beginning, several groups here and
there over the United States started to reconsider school
mathematics. They drafted new textbooks in mimeographed
form and made experiments with small groups of students
to find out what could be taught successfully to high school
and even elementary school students. The following groups
in particular made names for themselves in the revitalizing
of school mathematics:

> the University of Illinois, the School Mathematics
> Study Group at Yale University, the Greater Cleve-
> land Mathematics Project, the Madison Project, spon-
> sored jointly by Syracuse University and Webster

College, and the Boston College Mathematics Institute.

The "new math" has produced considerable alteration in the content of traditional school mathematics: arithmetic, algebra, geometry, trigonometry, college algebra, and solid geometry. Much of geometry, most of trigonometry, much of college algebra, and almost all of solid geometry have been omitted. The new math has inserted some discussion and development of 50 to 150 important and interesting comcepts of mathematics developed in the last 200 years. The new math has tried hard to make the methods of teaching mathematics in school imaginative and creative, and to stimulate investigation and discovery by young students. And at least some topics of important parts of mathematics usually taught in the first year of college, such as calculus and analytic geometry, have been pushed down into the last year of high school.

What Is Some of the New Math?

One of the immensely important ideas of mathematics, the idea of a *mathematical system* or structure, is introduced in the new math. This consists of:

- a set of mathematical entities;
- a small number of statements which are taken without requiring proof or assumptions;
- the task or problem of finding out the interesting deductions that can be drawn from this simple beginning.

For example, here is a mathematical system:

1) the five entities 0, 1, 2, 3, 4;

2) tables for addition and multiplication (see facing page).

What can we show that is interesting about this system? Well, among the statements that we can prove (by enumerat-

Addition

$A + B$		2nd element B				
		0	1	2	3	4
1st element A	0	0	1	2	3	4
	1	1	2	3	4	0
	2	2	3	4	0	1
	3	3	4	0	1	2
	4	4	0	1	2	3

Multiplication

$A \times B$		2nd element B				
		0	1	2	3	4
1st element A	0	0	0	0	0	0
	1	0	1	2	3	4
	2	0	2	4	1	3
	3	0	3	1	4	2
	4	0	4	3	2	1

ing all the cases and checking them, for example) are:

1) Every result of adding and multiplying operations, no matter how many, is still one of the original five entities: 0, 1, 2, 3, and 4.

This, of course, is very unlike ordinary arithmetic. In arithmetic the number of mathematical entities (the numbers 3, 9685, 428,571, and all the others) is not finite, and the result of any addition or multiplication of two positive whole numbers is always bigger than either of the numbers we started with.

Another property that we can prove is:

2) If A and B are any two entities in our system, and if $+$ stands for addition according to the addition table above, and $\times$ stands for multiplication according to the multiplication table above, then

$$A + B = B + A \text{ and } A \times B = B \times A$$

for every choice of A and B.

How do we prove this? One way is to take each of the 25 cases for addition and each of the 25 cases for multiplication and check them one by one. Is $1 + 2$ the same as $2 + 1$? Yes, according to the addition table, both are equal to 3. Is $3 + 2$ the same as $2 + 3$? Yes, according to the addition table, both are equal to 0. And so on. (Another way of proving this more quickly is to observe that each of the tables is *symmetric* about the diagonal from upper left to bottom right: if we should put a mirror all along that line, all the values in the lower left triangle would duplicate exactly all the values in the upper right triangle.) The name of this property is the *commutative law*. This property is true in ordinary arithmetic also.

An even "more interesting" property (this is an opinion, of course, because it is not possible to prove that something is more interesting than something else) is this one:

3) Given any two elements A and B, it is possible to find in all cases exactly one element X which has the property that $A + X = B$.

For example, if A is 3 and B is 2, then X is 4, because according to the addition table above, $3 + 4 = 2$, and also no other element added to 3 gives 2. This property can be proved easily by examining all the cases in this small mathematical system. The name of this property is the *unique inverse for addition*. In ordinary arithmetic we obtain unique inverses for addition only by using negative numbers.

The name of the mathematical system of five elements we have just described is the "Modulo 5 System."

Another important example of a mathematical system is the system of points, lines, and curves in plane geometry. For many people this example is more familiar than the Modulo 5 System because they have studied geometry. But geometry is a big mathematical system, and in many ways complicated, and it is easier to grasp the essential nature of mathematical systems by study of small examples like the Modulo 5 System instead of big ones like geometry.

The idea of mathematical system is a pattern that unifies many parts of mathematics. For example, over and over again we find in mathematics what are called *isomorphisms* (which is a word that means "same shape"): namely, we find instances where one mathematical system is just like another mathematical system; and then all the properties that can be proved in one are immediately provable in the other.

The Concepts Included in the New Math

In general, the concepts included in the new math have the following properties:
1) They have mathematical importance and lead to greater and more basic understanding of mathematics.
2) They permit simple examples so that young students, even children, can grasp the idea.
3) They have been discovered or developed intensively in the last 200 years.
4) They help give young people who stop studying mathematics when they leave high school a much better understanding of the meaning, power, and interest of mathematics.

These are important properties, of course. How well do the advocates and experimenters of the new math succeed?

Evaluation of the New Math

In the first place, it is too soon to evaluate the new math. It takes many years to test in practice any new system of education. In the case of the change from the phonetic method of teaching reading to the look-and-say method, the change itself, the observation of the poor results, and the beginning of the return to the phonetic method have taken more than a third of a century. For many years to come, the persons who never learned to read well because they were taught by the look-and-say method in the years 1930 to 1960 will remain in our society.

Second, a great deal of learning mathematics depends, of

course, on the teacher and how well he teaches. Many teachers teach so inspiringly that even a dry or difficult subject becomes interesting, exciting, and alive under their influence. Other teachers teach so badly that they convert interesting subjects to matter dry as dust and as repellent. In the long run, these two kinds of teaching may balance out; but in general, since the better teachers will try the newer methods, there may be a spurious effect—because if better teachers teach the new math for the first ten years and worse teachers teach the old math, it may appear that better results were produced from the new math when really it was the better teaching that produced them.

Third, there is a great deal of variation, of course, in students. Some students cannot be stopped from learning mathematics. Something about it appeals to them—perhaps the excitement of finding a subject where statements are TRUE, and can really be PROVED, and you can RELY on what you find out—like the formula $a^2 - b^2 = (a + b) \times (a - b)$, which is completely true in arithmetic for every a and b. Other students are repelled by mathematics. The variation in students makes it harder to demonstrate the effectiveness of the new math.

Perhaps it can eventually be shown that the ordinary student actually does profit from being taught the new math. Perhaps it can eventually be shown that he does not lose too much from less thorough teaching and smaller doses of arithmetic, algebra, geometry, and trigonometry. It will take many years for the demonstration. When students now ten and 15 years old become 35 and 40, there may be sufficient evidence for making a sound judgment.

On net balance, however, it is certainly hard to believe that the new math can do much harm, because the harm from teaching the old math has been very great. Also, with adding machines, desk calculating machines, and automatic computers, it is unreasonable to spend as much time on arithmetic as used to be spent. And certainly the knowledge of many proofs in solid geometry is not as useful as knowledge about mathematical systems in general.

Basic Principles of Teaching School Mathematics

In any case, it seems to me that the most important parts of teaching school mathematics are:

1) *Examples.* The teacher should give and explain a lot of good and interesting examples. The foundation of learning both for animals and human beings seems to be examples.

2) *Practice.* The student should have a lot of practice in using the mathematical ideas taught from the examples, and in solving problems in which those ideas occur. What is too much practice for one student may be far less than what is needed for another.

3) *Summarizing.* The student should construct for himself a correct and complete summary of the ideas taught. The capstone of understanding something is to be able to summarize its essence.

4) *Generalized Approach.* The student should be trained how to approach with his own resources a topic in mathematics that is completely new to him. We do not know what topics in mathematics we may have to understand in the future; it is desirable to learn a general method for coming to grips with any mathematical topic. (There is a general method; see Appendix 2, "Studying by Yourself.")

5) *Correctness.* The teacher should continually train the student to check and verify his work, making sure that it is right.

If this point of view is valid, then any fairly reasonable content of school mathematics can be justified. The really important thing is to teach it better, more thoroughly, with more understanding by the student and with more training to get correct results. In other words, the content of school mathematics is less important than teaching mathematical behavior: learning the kinds of steps and their sequence that lead to a deductive result that one can rely on.

A person with good mathematical training should be able to enter easily into the beginning parts of almost any mathematical topic, if it is adequately explained.

Correctness

Of these five parts of the teaching of school mathematics, the most important one is related to the way one's own work links with the work of others in society. This is correctness.

After I have done some mathematical work, I never accept it without reviewing it carefully. I ask myself here and there all the way through:

Is this right?

Have I made any mistakes?

Can I check this result some other way?

Far too many teachers, I believe, allow their students to pass through their courses year after year without continually insisting on thoroughly correct results. They forgive their students for sloppy work. They do not teach their students the habit and the necessity of achieving correct results.

The world outside of school has little use for wrong results, no matter how good the intentions.

Predicting the Future, and Running Risks

22

BEFORE WE PROCEED to the last chapter of this book "The Future and Mathematics," it is necessary for us to take a little side excursion and consider how we can estimate or predict the future. We here need to put together some of the ideas we talked about earlier under two headings, Estimating and Probability.

One of the most fruitful applications of mathematics is foretelling what will happen in the future. Sometimes we obtain exact predictions, as when astronomers using mathematics can foretell just when six months from a given date a spacecraft will fly past Mars. Sometimes we obtain approximate predictions, as when actuaries (the mathematicians of life insurance companies) can foretell about how many out of a thousand people now alive and aged 25 will still be alive 40 years from now, at age 65. Often, in fact, by making estimates based on what is happening now and what can be scientifically expected year after year, we can apply mathematics to foretell what will happen. The predictions made with good data to start with and sound methods to proceed with are far better than the predictions of gypsies, politicians, clairvoyants, generals, astrologists, and other people who are not using objective data and scientific and mathematical laws for their predictions.

288 | *Mathematics and the Environment*

Exact Predictions

A common everyday example of mathematical predicting which you and I and everybody else engage in almost unconsciously is predicting whether a moving car or one's self walking will get to an intersection first. We notice how the approaching car appears to move against the background of scenery. If the car appears to move forward in regard to the background, we know the car will get to the intersection first. If on the contrary the car seems to move backward in regard to the background, then we know we will get to the intersection first.

This is a case of exact predicting, or projection, and is often easy and simple. To expect the smooth continuance of what is happening is very much of a habit even in the ordinary everyday world.

But the case where we need to make approximate predictions based on probabilities is outside of our everyday experience and habits; and this case needs to be examined closely, for it is very important.

Approximate Predictions

Let's begin with this problem:

PROBLEM 1: John Jones wants to persuade Priscilla Smith to marry him. She says she is determined not to get married. But he decides that his chance of persuading her in any week to say yes is 1/10, and that he will ask her once each week, week after week for a year. What is the chance that she will marry him in one year's time?

Here's another problem with the same pattern:

PROBLEM 2: A group of engineers of the Transylvania Army has strung a communication line along a position which is being bombarded by the enemy every day. The line needs to last ten days. The chance of its being hit on any day is estimated as 1/20. What is the chance that the line will be cut in ten days?

Here's another problem with still the same pattern:

PROBLEM 3:   Harrison Jones is trying to throw double six with two dice. He has been given five throws to succeed. What is his chance of throwing double six in five throws?

A Pattern in Approximate Prediction: the "Eventually" Pattern

This kind of pattern is characteristic of many problems of prediction. The pattern is this: On the first trial or experiment, we see if some event happens. If it does not happen on the first trial, we see if the event happens on the second trial. If it does not happen on the second trial, we see if the event happens on the third trial. And so on, for a total of N trials.

In the first problem, the event is marrying, and there is one trial every week for 52 weeks.

In the second problem, the event is breaking of the line, and there is one trial or experiment each day for ten days.

In the third problem, the event is throwing double six, and there is a total of five throws.

We have used N to stand for the total number of trials. Let us make use of two more letters:

Let P be the chance of the event happening at any one trial or experiment. Let Q be the chance of the event not happening at that trial.

Since the event must either happen or not happen, P plus Q is equal to the probability of certainty, or 1.

The values of P, Q, and N for each of the three problems are shown in Table 1 on page 290.

From our ordinary everyday experience, we can see that whenever we consider whether some kind of thing will "eventually" happen, we are very likely to be considering

TABLE 1

Problem	Event	Chance P	Chance Q	Number N
1	Marriage	1/10	9/10	52 (weeks)
2	Cutting	1/20	19/20	10 (days)
3	Throwing double six	1/36	35/36	5 (throws)

a situation that has this important pattern of events. Sometimes we want the event to happen; hence comes the proverb "If at first you don't succeed, try, try again." Sometimes we do not want the event to happen; hence comes the proverb, "If you run a risk long enough, the danger will surely happen."

The Solution to Problems of This Pattern

In order to see how to deal with this problem in general, let us first take the simplest case, Problem 3 on page 289. Rephrasing:

PROBLEM 3: What is the chance of throwing double six with two dice, at least once in five throws?

Solution: The chance P of throwing double six with two dice on any particular throw is 1/36, because there are 36 possible patterns for the dice to come down (such as 1, 3 or 2, 5, or 5, 2) and only one of the patterns, 6, 6, is double 6.

The chance Q of not throwing double six in the first throw is $= 1 - 1/36$ or 35/36

The chance of not throwing double six in the second throw is, of course, the same, 35/36, Q

The chance of not throwing double six in either the first throw or the second throw:

> EQUALS (the chance of not throwing double six in the first throw) TIMES (the chance of not throwing double six in the second throw) $= 35/36 \times 35/36 = Q^2$

Similarly, the chance of not throwing double six in any of

the first three throws is $35/36 \times 35/36 \times 35/36 = Q^3$

The chance of not throwing double six in any of the first five throws is: $35/36 \times 35/36 \times 35/36 \times 35/36 \times 35/36 = Q^5$

Finally, the chance of throwing at least one double six in five throws is: ONE MINUS (this chance) $= 1 - Q^5$

In order to calculate this chance numerically, we need to multiply 35/36 (which equals .972 as a decimal) by itself for a total of five factors, which equals $(.972)^5$. To estimate the result easily, we can use Table 2 (below), a table of prepared results.

Column 4 in the table shows that $(.97)^5$ is .8587. Column 3 shows that $(.99)^5$ is .9510. .972 is located 1/10 of the distance

TABLE 2

The Effect of Running Risks: Q to the Nth Power

P:	.001	.003	.01	.03	.1	.3	.5
Q:	.999	.997	.99	.97	.9	.7	.5
N							
1	.9990	.9970	.9900	.9700	.9000	.7000	.5000
2	.9980	.9940	.9801	.9409	.8100	.4900	.2500
3	.9970	.9910	.9703	.9127	.7290	.3430	.1250
5	.9950	.9851	.9510	.8587	.5905	.1681	.03125
10	.9900	.9704	.9044	.7374	.3487	.02825	.0009766
20	.9802	.9417	.8179	.5438	.1216	.0007979	0
30	.9704	.9138	.7397	.4010	.04239	.00002254	0
50	.9512	.8605	.6050	.2181	.005154	0	0
100	.9048	.7405	.3660	.04755	.00002656	0	0
200	.8186	.5483	.1340	.002261	0	0	0
300	.7407	.4060	.04904	.0001075	0	0	0
500	.6064	.2226	.006570	0	0	0	0
1000	.3677	.04956	.00004317	0	0	0	0

NOTE: 0 has been used for numbers that are smaller than .00001.

from .97 to .99; so it is reasonable to estimate that $(.972)^5$ is located 1/10 of the distance from .8587 to .9510. Carrying out the prorata arithmetic:

$$
\begin{array}{r}
.9510 \\
-.8587 \\
\hline
.0923
\end{array}
\qquad
\begin{array}{r}
.8587 \\
+.0092 \\
\hline
.8679
\end{array}
$$

1/10 of .0923 = .0092

So we can estimate that 35/36 to the 5th power is close to .8679 or .87.

This is the chance of *not* throwing double six at all in five throws. So the chance of throwing at least one double six in five throws is:

ONE MINUS (this chance)

which is equal to:

$$1 - .87, \text{ or } .13$$

which is about one chance in eight.

We can generalize our solving procedure with a formula:

If Q is the chance of some event not happening in one trial, then Q raised to the Nth power (Q^N) is the chance of that event not happening in every one of N trials, and ONE MINUS (Q to the Nth power) $= 1 - Q^N$ is the chance of the event happening at least once in the N trials.

The Chances of Life and Death

Perhaps the greatest importance of this pattern is that it is the pattern of life and death, survival or disappearance. Here is an example:

PROBLEM 4: A child is born at age zero. What is the chance that he will die before age 70?

Solution: It is no longer true in this problem that the chance Q of surviving from one year to the next is the same from year to year. Instead, we have different chances of surviving from year to year. An extract from a modern statistical table of annual survival chances is shown in Table 3, on facing page.

But the method of multiplying the survival chances together is still completely valid, and so:

(the chance of surviving to age 70) IS $Q_0 \times Q_1 \times Q_2 \times Q_3 \times \ldots \times Q_{68} \times Q_{69}$ where Q_0 is the chance of surviving from age 0 to age one, Q_1 is the chance of surviving

TABLE 3

Chances According to the Mortality Table Called the Commissioners 1958 Standard Ordinary Mortality Table

Age	Q Chance of Surviving for One Year	P Chance of Dying in That Year As a decimal fraction:	P Chance of Dying in That Year In Words:
0	.9929	.0071	7 chances in 1000
1	.9982	.0018	
2	.9985	.0015	
5	.9986	.0014	
10	.9988	.0012	12 chances in 10,000
20	.9982	.0018	
30	.9979	.0021	2 chances in 1000
40	.9965	.0035	
50	.9917	.0083	
60	.9797	.0203	2 chances in 100
70	.9502	.0498	5 chances in 100
80	.8900	.1100	
85	.8388	.1612	
90	.7719	.2281	about 1 chance in 5
95	.6488	.3512	about 1 chance in 3
99	0	1	certain to die

from age one to age two, and in general for any year i, Q_i is the chance of surviving from age i to age $i + 1$. And the chance of death before age 70 is:

ONE MINUS (the chance of surviving to age 70)

We can estimate this chance, making use of Table 3. But first, a word about Table 3.

Table 3 is an extract from a *mortality table*, a table showing the annual rate of mortality, i.e., the annual death rate. This particular mortality table was put together in 1958 by a committee of insurance commissioners representing the states of the United States. This table was based on the experience of many large life insurance companies under a kind of life insurance policy called ordinary insurance, which insured what are called standard risks, the lives of persons not having impairments such as overweight, heart disease, etc.

We can see as we look at Table 3 that there are about

seven chances in a thousand of a baby's dying in the first year of life. This is reasonable: a baby can have a rough time in the first year of life. About age ten, the chance of dying in a year of age appears to go to its lowest point, about 12 chances in 10,000. Then the chance of dying in a given year of age goes higher and higher and higher, until around age 95, the chance is about one in three that a person of that age will die in the next year. At age 99, the table states that the chance is one, meaning that it is certain that a person aged 99 will die in the next year. This, of course, is not true, but in making this particular table of mortality the experts making the table decided that it was sensible and convenient for their purposes to make this assumption. The main purpose they had in mind was that this table would be used in life insurance companies for making sure that reserves were adequate for insuring people; and this assumption is sensible for that purpose.

How to Multiply Many Chances Together

Let us return now to the problem of estimating the chance of surviving from birth to age 70.

We have to multiply together 70 numbers representing the chance of surviving one year. These are:

(1) the chance of surviving one year from age 0 to age one;
(2) the chance of surviving one year from age one to age two;
(3) the chance of surviving one year from age two to age three; and so on, up to
(70) the chance of surviving one year from age 69 to age 70.

Only ten of these numbers are shown in Table 3. What shall we do?

First, we can estimate what the missing numbers are. And second, we can multiply them together.

Looking at Table 3, we can see that the largest of these numbers probably is the chance of surviving from age ten to age 11, which is given in the table as .9988, and the small-est of these numbers is probably very close to the chance of surviving one year from age 70 to age 71, which is given in the table as .9502. As we look over the column of the chances of survival from one year to the next, we can reasonably con-clude that the first 50 of the numbers we desire to multiply together are between .9988 and .9917 and that the last 20 numbers are between .9917 and .9502. So let's settle there-fore for multiplying together:

(1) 50 numbers equal to .997 (which seems like a typical figure to choose for ages 0 to 49); and

(2) 20 numbers equal to .977 (which seems like a typical figure to choose for ages 50 to 69).

The procedure we have just used is a general procedure. If we have many different numbers to multiply together which are all between, say, 9/10 and 1, we can choose typical numbers and repeat them over and over in groups.

Now, how shall we carry out this multiplication of 70 numbers in a simple way? Well, we can use some of the prepared results in Table 2, page 291.

1) We take from column (2), on the line for N equal to 50:
$(.997)^{50} = .8605$

2) We take from column (3), on the line for N equal to 20:
$(.99)^{20} = .8179$

3) We take from column (4), on the line for N equal to 20:
$(.97)^{20} = .5438$

4) We estimate $(.977)^{20}$ from .8179, Item 2, and .5438, Item 3, by linear interpolation.

5) The difference between .8179 and .5438 is .2741

6) The difference between .990 and .970 is .020; we want the value for .977, which is 7/20 of the distance be-tween .970 and .990.

7) So we find 7/20 of Item 5, the difference, .2741, and this is equal to .0959

8) We add .0959 to .5438, and this gives .6397 for our estimate of $(.977)^{20}$

9) Now all we have to do is to multiply together Item 1, .8605, and Item 8, .6397; this is equal to .5505, which is approximately equal to .55

So we can estimate the chance of living from age 0 to age 70 according to this table as 55 chances out of a hundred, and therefore the chance of dying is 45 chances out of a hundred.

The Extinction of Man?

In the next chapter we will talk about the future and mathematics, and we raise the questions: What will the world of man be like in a thousand years? What part will mathematics play in it?

However, before we leave the question of running risks, we have one final and very important question to try to answer, in order to make any reasonable estimates about the future a thousand years distant. And that is: Will mankind be on the earth a thousand years from now? Or will mankind be extinct?

What is the evidence and the reasoning which may help to answer this question?

Life has never been safe or guaranteed for any species of living being. Although it is true that there has been a great increase in the species man from a few million members in 5000 B.C. to over 3 billion members now, other species — like the dinosaurs and the trilobites — once dominated the earth and later disappeared. In the course of the earth's history, far more species have become extinct than have survived.

The world of man went through a turning point in August 1945, when the first nuclear bomb was exploded over Hiroshima, Japan. It was equivalent in explosive force to 20,000 tons of TNT. It killed immediately about 70,000 persons; and over the next few days, months, and years it directly caused the death of at least another 100,000 persons, from fallout, radioactivity, burns, leukemia, etc.

Since 1945, the explosive power of an individual nuclear bomb has increased more than a thousand times, and hundreds of nuclear-bomb test explosions have taken place. Nuclear weapons are rated in explosive power according to millions of tons of TNT equivalent, called *megatons*. Apparently the most powerful nuclear bomb actually exploded in the 20-year period 1945-65 was a 60-megaton bomb; and if it had been surrounded with a uranium jacket instead of a lead jacket, it would have been a 100-megaton bomb. According to Prof. Amitai Etzioni of Columbia University, in his book *The Hard Way to Peace* (page 278):

> A 50-megaton bomb explosion would wipe out entire regions and their populations through massive fire damage far exceeding the heavy destruction wreaked by blast alone. . . . The 50-megaton bomb represents only a small step in the direction of building bombs that could destroy regions and nations in one nuclear strike. Theoretically there is no limitation on the size bomb that can be built.

The quantity of nuclear weapons stockpiled in the United States and in the Soviet Union is enough to kill all human beings. It has been estimated that the explosive power of these stockpiles is equivalent to more than 20 tons of TNT for every man, woman, and child on this earth.

If only a few percent of these nuclear weapons were exploded here and there all over the earth, the spreading radioactive fallout would kill all human beings and almost all life, except certain highly resistant forms like the cockroach and the wireworm.

Other countries are joining the "Nuclear Club." Great Britain, France, and China have exploded nuclear devices of their own manufacture. It has been estimated that at least five more nations have the scientific and industrial capacity to make nuclear weapons in the years 1966 to 1970.

No international control over the use of nuclear weapons exists. Any government able to make them or buy them can use them if it chooses; and there are now more than 120 governments on the earth. In fact, it seems clear that no government with nuclear weapons will accept defeat without using them.

Not only does nuclear warfare cast a black shadow over the future of man, but so does chemical, bacteriological, and radiological warfare—nerve gases, deadly diseases cultivated in laboratories, Cobalt 60, which is intensely radioactive for long periods. It seems as if, just as mankind has begun to solve the age-old problems of scarcity of food, clothing, shelter, and the other needs and wants of life, so mankind has solved the problem of how to make wars so destructive that almost no human beings can survive them.

The hazard that men will become extinct is clear and obvious.

How shall we estimate the chance?

The Chance of Extinction

Up until 1945 it was physically impossible for human beings to unleash a catastrophe powerful enough to make mankind extinct. Beginning in 1945, and completely true nowadays, this power to do so resides in at least two governments and is spreading.

The risk of nuclear weapons being used in a big war is serious. In fact, two nuclear bombs were used in 1945 in Japan. The last hundred years have seen at least three major wars in which heavily industrialized powers fought each other in unlimited conflict: the war of 1870-71, between France and Germany; World War I, 1914-18; and World War II, 1939-45. Such war has begun in three out of the last hundred years (1870, 1914, 1939). We could perhaps estimate the risk as one out of 33. Who would travel in a motor car if one mile out of every 33 miles traveled resulted in death? Who would fly in an airplane if one out of every 33 flights resulted in a crash killing all persons on board?

Yet we are willy-nilly riding on a planet, where the two major wars that have broken out since 1900 have resulted in a death toll of over 20 million for World War I and over 40 million for World War II. Large-scale nuclear war between nations will dwarf these figures: hundreds of millions of deaths will occur in a few hours.

But let's be conservative, and tentatively estimate the chance of mankind becoming extinct in any year not as 1/33 but as 1/100.

PROBLEM 5:   If the chance of an event happening over a year is 1/100, what is the chance that it will happen at least once over a thousand years?

Solution: The chance of the event not happening for each of a thousand years is: [(the chance that it will not happen in the first year, which is 99/100) TIMES (the chance that it will not happen in the second year, which is 99/100) TIMES (the chance that it will not happen in the third year, which is 99/100), and so on, year after year . . . TIMES (the chance that it will not happen in the thousandth year, which is 99/100)]. So what we have to do is multiply 99/100 by itself 1000 times, and subtract it from 1.

Looking back in Table 2, we find that (99/100) to the 1000th power is equal to .00004317, which is about four chances in 100,000.

The chance therefore of the event's happening in the next thousand years is ONE MINUS (this chance) or .99996, almost certain.

No matter what the chance is, it can be seen from Table 2 (and can easily be proved mathematically) that all we have to do is to run the risk long enough, and the danger is almost certain to happen. In other words, if we tempt fate long enough, fate will surely snatch us.

Not only this year and next year but year after year for a hundred and a thousand years and longer still, human beings must avoid the use of nuclear and other weapons for purposes of major war, or mankind will surely become extinct.

The problem of avoiding this extreme disaster is clearly the most important problem we have mentioned in this book so far. And the mathematical predictions that govern this problem are worth a great deal of thoughtful attention.

The Future and Mathematics

IF WE COULD LOOK AHEAD a thousand years, what would
we see for mathematics and the future?

What will the future be like, and what part will mathematics play in it?

Will two and two still be four, or will it become something else?

How much of life will be influenced by mathematics?

Will everybody be a mathematician?

If There Is a Future for Man . . .

Let us make the assumption that there will be no large-
scale nuclear war or similar holocaust for a thousand years,
and that therefore civilization and mankind will not become
extinct. This is an assumption not founded on reasonable
predictions; see the discussion in the preceding chapter.
But let us make this assumption just the same.

From this assumption it follows that a large measure of
peace and friendliness among human beings will actually
operate. The principles of live and let live, of altruism and
enlightened selfishness, of mutual respect and cooperation
will become viable and practical principles. Why? Basically
because the outpouring of scientific technology and understanding will produce plenty for everybody. If there is plenty

301

for both you and me, why should we fight? Instead "we can go to the stars together."

Under these conditions we can see obvious trends in the development of a thousand more years of scientific technology, as compared with the short two hundred years of such technology that we benefit by today.

The Physical World

In a thousand years, under this assumption, the earth will be a garden of Paradise. The four seasons—winter, spring, summer, and autumn—will still be with us. But there will be control over weather and rainfall, so that droughts will be nonexistent; many lands now arid will become fertile with rain; and many parts of the world will have atmospheres artificially modified to improve the climate for human beings.

Both land and sea will be skillfully cultivated to produce food and raw materials. Plenty of energy will be available for most enterprises. Ample materials, both raw and manufactured, will be available. Waste and pollution, destruction and spoliation of the environment, will be greatly reduced, if not eliminated.

Most of the species of larger living things will live only with the permission and approval of man. All the insects and microorganisms that harm man will be entirely gone. Cancer, heart disease, and other plagues of today will be entirely gone.

Space travel will be common. Settlements by men on some of the planets and satellites of the solar system will be operating. Perhaps the first human expedition to the stars will have set forth.

Human population will be stabilized at an optimum level. Hunger and malnutrition will be gone. Poverty will be gone. Crime will be almost nonexistent. The genetic quality of human beings will be greatly improved; no longer will one out of 200 human infants be born with genetic defects. Persons desiring children will be able to select from their sperms and ova to choose the inheritance of their children. Artificial species of life will have been created from our knowledge of genes, chromosomes and nucleic acids.

The Social World

Everywhere the system of society will be: From each according to his capacity and the needs of society to use his capacity; to each according to his own needs and his reasonable desires.

Unpleasant work will be minor; it may last for two or three years in youth—like military service today. But there will be no armies; there will simply be a world police force. Leisure, sport, travel, experience, discovery, and creation will be a great part of life. Almost all factories will be automatic.

The guidance of society will be contained basically in the programming of giant computers, which will follow out plans for the optimizing and enriching of the life of every individual. These will not be stifling, rigid plans but flexible, creative ones, allowing for as many choices as may be appealing to the individual. The plans will provide incentives and stimulation where appropriate.

People will have much more individual freedom than now exists in either autocratic or democratic countries, just as today a man experiences an immense increase of freedom when he does not have to spend all his waking moments in plowing the fields and growing crops to raise enough food for his family and his farm animals.

The Intellectual World

Education will be an exciting introduction to knowledge and the acquisition of skills. The best teaching of our day will be the normal teaching of the future.

The golden time of youth in school will be used well. Excellent instruction, sights, sounds, trips, games, practices — first-hand opportunities to try a great variety of interesting and useful activities — will be fully available to students, in a way that will match their interests and talents. The great ideas of centuries of human culture will be brought home meaningfully to almost all young people.

The languages that human beings use will be considerably improved. One of the greatest improvements in language will be the ability to create words that are needed for ideas, even in instances where our present habits prevent us: for example, a single word in English that will stand for "he or she or him or her" without specifying grammatical gender and case.

Even the highest forms of intelligence will be displayed by programmed computers, which will incorporate the wisdom of many generations of human society and make it accessible.

The answers to a great many of the problems that we argue about nowadays will be calculated by computers. The failures of human minds to understand each other and agree on reasonable judgments will be analyzed essentially into differences in the way these minds perceive situations and make decisions about them. Then these differences will be referred to programmed computers and largely reconciled in the way that children often have their differences resolved by impartial, friendly, and understanding adults. All the language of thought will be calculable, like mathematics.

The Place of Mathematics in the Future

From this outline of the future world we foresee, it is clear that mathematics will play a large and important part in this new world. Mathematics plays a small part in simple worlds like those of the hunter and the farmer; it plays a much larger part in a complex world, like that of the engineer and the scientist. Although many sections of the complex world of the future will be like the ordinary telephone (almost all of us know how to use it and almost none of us know how it works), yet the section of the future complex world that we shall have most to do with will be understood with the help of mathematical ideas. A cowboy riding a horse does not need much mathematics, but an astronaut needs to know calculus.

Mathematical Ideas Used in the Future World

A great many of the mathematical ideas we use today will inevitably be present in the future world also. For example:
    the number 2
    a circle
    pi, 3.14159265 . . .
    the square root of minus one
will all be there.

It seems likely that the same Arabic numerals that human beings use almost universally today will still be used by human beings a thousand years from now. After all, the Arabic numerals have already had a thousand years of use, even if their shapes were slightly different a thousand years ago.

Two plus two will still equal four. There is, of course, no way in which a mathematical truth, like two plus two equals four, can change over a thousand years or even longer. For not only is this a mathematical truth, following from definitions and reasoning, but it is also a summary of a general property of the real world: two objects considered together with two other objects count up to four objects. Even if the language in which this statement was made should change as much as the Latin of A.D. 100 has changed into the English of today, still the underlying truth would remain unchanged.

It is quite likely that new, important, and useful branches of mathematics at present undiscovered or unrecognized will exist in the world of mathematics of a thousand years from now. For example, since 1800, at least two important branches of mathematics, hardly anticipated, have come into existence: statistics and symbolic logic, which includes the "algebra of classes." I believe that an "algebra of states and events" will soon (or has already) come into existence.

The Number of Mathematical Ideas
Learned and Understood

Almost all the young people of a thousand years from now will absorb not only arithmetic but at least 500 and maybe a thousand or 1200 of the interesting, important, and useful ideas of mathematics, such as the idea of a variable and the idea of a function. They will absorb these ideas as naturally as you and I absorb the ideas of 70, 2/3, and ten below zero.

Although there will still be differences between those people who make mathematics their career in life and those who do not, "everybody will be a mathematician." Everybody will be capable of appreciating a mathematical or logical argument that is not too long or too complex. Everybody will understand and enjoy many mathematical recreations. Everybody will use at least 500 mathematical ideas. In ordinary conversation the word "integral" will be as acceptable as the word "sum."

A crowning achievement of the coming together of mathematics and scientific technology is the programmed automatic computer. Even today, in its infancy, it can do vast quantities of mental work. A thousand years from now computers will do all mental work except a tiny fraction. They will converse in natural language and deal logically in all kinds of ideas. To make full use of the amazing computer powers of the future will require a great many human beings who have had extensive training in mathematics and programming.

Reasons for Expecting This Kind of Mathematical Future

There are several valid reasons for expecting the kind of mathematical future that we have outlined in this chapter (provided that the more likely future of the extinction of man does not happen).

First, we can look back at the role of mathematics in more than 5000 years of human culture and history. Every feature of mathematics which has arisen in those years, and which has been shown to be a logical part of the mathematical description of the world or its contents, will surely continue. Arithmetic has existed since prehistory. Geometry has existed since the ancient Greeks. Algebra has existed since the medieval Arabs. The reasoning of mathematics has been and can be verified in a multitude of cases, and proved logically besides. No mathematical theorem which has been rigorously proved true at one time can be proved false at a later time.

Second, we have seen during the years beginning in 1944 the start of the automatization of mathematics brought about by the computer. Much more is bound to happen. The evidence is convincing that any defined operation of mathematics or reasoning that a human being can perform, a computer can also perform, and do it much faster, on a much larger scale, and much more reliably. After all, there is nothing supernatural about a human brain. And if one type of structure in the real world can do something—showing that it is possible—is it not likely that other types of structures in the real world may also be able to do it?

Third, mathematics is in many ways a general description of the real world, particularly the operations of counting and measuring, and their implications. We have seen enough evidence to be convinced that the general description will not change substantially. For example, no matter what new science may develop, and no matter what kinds of objects it may deal with, we can be certain that in that new science three objects and four objects taken together will be seven objects. In other words, arithmetic is bound to work in any new science, whatever it may be. The same is true for other parts of mathematics.

Finally, the immense forces of scientific and technological development in human affairs make use everywhere of mathematics as underpinning and foundation. How can you have a structure without a foundation? Mathematics will inevitably remain part of the foundations of science and technology. And it will always remain, as the philosopher and mathematician Alfred North Whitehead once said, the way in which we "weigh the stars and count the billions of molecules in a drop of water."

APPENDICES

APPENDIX 1

A Short Introduction to Algebra

Algebra - Kinds of Algebra - The Start of Algebra - Parentheses -
The Basic Rules of Algebra - Powers - Expressions - Algebraic
Multiplication - Algebraic Division - Factors - Equations

Algebra

QUESTION 1:   What is algebra?

Answer: Algebra is one of the most important, far-reaching and basic of the branches of mathematics. Typically its subject matter consists of:

1) unknown numbers represented by letters like a, b, c, x, and y; and combinations of them such as $3a$, which means 3 times a, whatever number a represents

2) operations, such as addition or multiplication of expressions involving letters, such as $3a$ times $5b$, which equals $15ab$

3) formulas, such as A equals L times W, AREA equals LENGTH times WIDTH

4) equations, such as: "If 3 times x equals 6, what does x equal?"

5) powers, such as a cubed, which is equal to a times a times a, or a squared, which is equal to a times a

6) various kinds of less familiar numbers including "negative" numbers such as "minus ten," or "ten below zero," "irrational" numbers such as "the square root of two," and "complex" numbers such as "three plus four times the square root of minus one"

Here are some sample problems in algebra:

1) If 7 x's and 3 y's equal 13, and 2 x's and 4 y's equal 10, what are x and y?

2) Show that for any pair of numbers a and b that you may care to choose, (a squared) minus (b squared) equals (a plus b) times (a minus b)

311

Algebra may be defined as the branch of mathematics in which quantities may be represented by letters, other kinds of numbers besides positive numbers may be used, and problems are characteristically solved by constructing equations and manipulating them.

Kinds of Algebra

QUESTION 2: Is there more than one kind of algebra?

Answer: Yes. The kind of algebra we have just been talking about has the name "elementary algebra." It is the commonest and most important variety of a collection of mathematical systems called algebras. An algebra is not restricted to the handling of numerical quantities; it may deal with other mathematical entities such as "statements" or "circuits" (for example, the algebra called Boolean algebra). And such algebras may have useful applications.

But algebra, unlike arithmetic, is always characterized by the use of letters to stand for variables. In any algebra, a letter may represent or stand for any number or entity in the class of things being discussed in the algebra; or a letter may be restricted to represent only one of a class of mathematical entities, the particular one which meets certain specified conditions.

QUESTION 3: What does the word "algebra" come from?

Answer: The word "algebra" comes from Medieval Latin, which in turn took it from the Arabic; it is a modification of the Arabic word *al-jebr* or *al-jabr*, meaning "bone-setting." The word thus refers to algebraic reduction or algebraic simplification, a simile derived from the fitting together of broken bones under skin and tissue where one could not see but had to operate with unknowns.

The Start of Algebra

QUESTION 4:   What is the very beginning of algebra?

Answer: The logical beginning of algebra is something like this:

Let a stand for any number; let b stand for any number (which may or may not be the same number). Then:

$a + b$ (read "a plus b") stands for the sum of the two numbers chosen, the sum of a and b.

$a - b$ (read "a minus b") means the first number a less the second number b, the result of subtracting b from a.

ab (read "ab"), with a and b written right next to each other and no sign between them, means a times b, the product of a and b, the result of multiplying a by b.

$a \cdot b$ (read "a dot b" — the dot being a centered dot, not a dot on the line like a period) is another way of designating the product of a and b. The dot is necessary sometimes to avoid confusion: for example the product of 4, 3, a, 2, and c needs to be written as $4 \cdot 3 \cdot a \cdot 2 \cdot c$

a/b (read "a over b") or $a \div b$ (read "a divided by b") means the result of dividing a by b.

a^n (read "a to the nth power") means a times a times a, and so on, for n occurrences of a.

Algebra then goes on to consider problems using letters (variables) and how to solve them. Such problems include:

Is $a^3 - b^3$ always the same as the product of $(a - b)$ times $(a^2 + ab + b^2)$? What is a value of x so that x times x equals two?

QUESTION 5:   What do the results or answers in algebra reduce to?

Answer: In arithmetic, of course, we can find out just what the results or answers reduce to; we calculate them numerically. This we cannot do in algebra: often we simply indicate the results. Until more information is obtained, we do not know the numerical value of results; we do not know what the expressions reduce to. But, curiously enough, this lack of information in algebra is often an advantage: it implies that whatever we manage to accomplish with a and b applies to all the numbers that a and b might stand for. For example, we know that for every a and b, $a^2 - b^2$ equals $(a + b)$ times $(a - b)$.

QUESTION 6: Can you use other letters, symbols and signs besides a and b?

Answer: Of course, you can use other letters. If the two numbers we started with had been labeled with different letters, say g and m, then $g + m$ (read "g plus m") would designate their sum. And similarly for the other combinations of symbols, $g - m$, gm, g/m.

QUESTION 7: In arithmetic, 47 with 4 and 7 written next to each other does not mean 4 times 7. Why is this different in algebra? And how would you represent the number 47 in algebraic language?

Answer: The main reason for using *adjacency* in algebra (the writing of one figure or letter right next to the other) as the sign of multiplication is that in algebra, unlike arithmetic, multiplication is the commonest indicated operation. So it saves a good deal of work to use the easiest sign, adjacency, for this meaning.

To write 47 in algebraic style, we would write $(4 \cdot 10) + 7$ meaning four times ten plus seven.

QUESTION 8: Why isn't the times sign of arithmetic, "×," used in algebra?

Answer: It is used every now and then, but only rarely. The main reason for avoiding it is that in handwriting its shape is likely to be confused with the commonest symbol in algebra for an unknown quantity, the letter x.

Parentheses

The sequence in which algebraic or arithmetical operations is performed makes a great deal of difference. In arithmetic, the sequence of operations is usually shown by the sequence of figures on a page, or by instructions, or by English words. But in algebra, the sequence of operations is regularly shown by the use of signs of grouping, *parentheses*, also called *mathematical parentheses*.

For example, what is one plus three times ten? This question has two meanings. By using more English words, we can distinguish between the two meanings:

1) one plus three, all multiplied by ten, which is four times ten, which is 40; and

2) one plus the product of three times ten, which is one plus thirty, or 31.

In algebra, however, we make use of signs of grouping, *parentheses:*

$$(1 + 3) \times 10 = 40, \text{ and}$$
$$1 + (3 \times 10) = 31.$$

The operations inside the parentheses are performed first.

There is a rule used in arithmetic that all multiplications and divisions indicated are to be performed first, and then all additions and subtractions indicated are to be performed second. This rule, also observed in algebra, cuts down the number of parentheses one needs to write. With this rule, $1 + (3 \times 10) = 31$ can also be correctly written: $1 + 3 \times 10 = 31$.

From time to time, expressions in parentheses have to be treated as new units in other expressions. Therefore parentheses with "stronger grouping," as the phrase goes, are used. The usual sequence is: ordinary parentheses ( ), square brackets [ ], curly brackets { }.

In the example:

$$\{[(1 + 2) \cdot 5 + 2] \cdot 5 + 2\} \cdot 5 + 2$$

the sequence of operations is:

Take 1; add 2; multiply by 5; add 2; multiply by 5; add 2; multiply by 5; add 2.

The result is 437.

In the example:

$$\{[1 + (2 \cdot 5 + 2)]5 + 2\} \cdot (5 + 2)$$

the sequence of operations is quite different, and the result is 469. A third variation is $1 + 2 \cdot 5 + 2 \cdot 5 + 2 \cdot 5 + 2$, which equals 33.

QUESTION 9: Why are mathematical parentheses important?

Answer: Because they show clearly just what we mean mathematically—just what expression we are designating. From time to time, in English writing, we have the same problem, especially in making clear which idea a modifier really modifies.

Consider the example:

The person who steals often is compelled to by need. Does the "often" modify "steals" or "is compelled to"? Using mathematical parentheses to show grouping, we can clearly express either one of the two meanings.

The person (WHO STEALS OFTEN) is compelled to by need.

The person (WHO STEALS) often is compelled to by need.

To write clear English however, we cannot use parentheses in this way; instead we have to change the order of words so as to obtain clear meaning:

The person who often steals is compelled to by need.

The person who steals is often compelled to by need.

The Basic Rules of Algebra

The rules of algebra are almost the same as the rules for arithmetic, because the subject matter of each consists of numbers as observed in the ordinary everyday world and extended by reasoning. But in algebra we possess a more precise language for stating the rules. Here are most of the basic rules of algebra:

1) It makes no difference in what sequence you add numbers together:
$$(a + b) + c = a + (b + c) = a + b + c$$
$$a + b = b + a$$

2) It makes no difference in what sequence you multiply numbers together:
$$(ab)c = a(bc) = abc$$
$$ab = ba$$

3) If you multiply a sum by a common factor, the result is the same as when you multiply each term contained in the sum by the same common factor:
$$(a + b)c = ac + bc$$

4) It is possible to subtract any number from any other number. Or, for any a and b, there exists a unique x such that $a + x = b$. This x equals the remainder from subtracting a from b, $b - a$.

5) It is possible to divide any number by any other number, except zero. Or, for any a and b, except a equal to zero, there exists a unique x such that $a \cdot x = b$; this x equals the quotient of b divided by a, b/a.

6) There exists a unique number zero (0). It has the properties that for every a:
$$a - a = 0$$
$$a \cdot 0 = 0.$$

7) There exists a unique number one (1). It has the property that:
$$a/a = 1, \text{ for every } a \text{ not equal to } 0.$$

8) Any number a times -1 equals $-a$; and -1 times -1 equals $+1$.

9) Equals (i.e., equal quantities) can be added to equals, subtracted from equals, multiplied by equals, and divided by equals (except that division by zero is excluded, not permitted), and the results are equals. In other words, if a equals b, and c is any number, then $a + c = b + c$, $a - c = b - c$, $ac = bc$, and $a/c = b/c$ (except in this last case c may not be zero).

Powers

A power of any number a is a multiplied by itself a certain number of times:

$a \times a \times a \ldots \times a$ where a occurs n times is written a^n and is read a to the nth power. n is called the *exponent* of the power.

a^2, a to the 2nd power, is $a \times a$ and is called a squared, or the *square* of a.

a^3, a to the 3rd power, is $a \times a \times a$, and is called a cubed, or the *cube* of a.

To multiply powers of a together you add their exponents. For example, $a^3 \times a^2$ equals a to the power 3 plus 2, which equals a to the 5th power, a^5; this is true because $a \times a \times a$ times $a \times a$ will have as result $a \times a \times a \times a \times a$.

To divide a^m by a^n, you subtract exponents: $a^m \div a^n = a^{m-n}$.

For example, a^6, $a \times a \times a \times a \times a \times a$, divided by a^4, $a \times a \times a \times a$, equals a^2, $a \times a$: $a^6 \div a^4 = a^{6-4} = a^2$.

a^0, a to the *zero power*, is equal to 1 for every a (not zero). This is a natural consequence of the definition of division. For example a^3 divided by $a^3 = a^{3-3} = a^0$ and is equal to 1, since a^3 divides exactly once into a^3.

a^1, a to the power 1, is a itself.

a to a negative power n, a^{-n}, is the same as 1 divided by a^n; that is, $a^{-n} = 1/a^n$.

a^{-1}, a to the power minus 1, is $1/a$, and is called the *reciprocal* of a.

$a^{1/2}$, a to the one-half power, is a number c such that $c \times c = a$, and is called the *square root* of a and is often denoted by $\sqrt{a}$ or $\sqrt[2]{a}$.

$a^{1/n}$, a to the power $1/n$, is a number r such that $r \times r \times r \ldots \times r$, with n occurrences of r, is equal to a. $a^{1/n}$ is called the nth root of a, and is sometimes written $\sqrt[n]{a}$.

QUESTION 10: Can you choose any number that you like

as the exponent of a power, and will the result have meaning?

Answer: In general, yes. It is a natural consequence of these definitions that any whole number or fraction, positive or negative, can be the exponent of a power of any number a. Of course, all the powers of 1 are 1 and all the powers of 0 (except the zeroth power) are 0. 0^0 (zero to the zeroth power) is not defined.

QUESTION 11: Suppose a is a negative number which is being raised to the power 1/2?

Answer: This leads to many interesting and advanced ideas. For more discussion of them, see a good textbook on algebra.

Expressions

An *expression* in algebra is a symbol or combination of symbols serving to designate some quantity. Here are some examples of expressions:

1) $3 + 7/8 - 2(5) = -6\,1/8$

This expression is made up only of specified numbers.

2) $7x^4 + 3.6y^2 + mxyz^2$

Each of the terms in this expression is made up of specified numbers together with letters for variables. This expression is a function since what it designates depends on x, y, m, and z. (See Chapter 11, "Functions and Graphs.")

3) $(a + b)^2 = a^2 + 6a + 9$

This expression is an equation. If $b = 3$, this equation is true for all values of a; if b is not equal to 3, it will be true for only some values of a and b.

4) $7x > 2x$, read "$7x$ is greater than $2x$"

This expression is a relation (true only if x is positive).

The word "expression" is convenient because of its generality; it names the objects that we deal with when we work in algebra. The word comes from the Latin *ex*, "out," and *premere*, "to press"; the derivation suggests the vivid idea of something squeezed out or pressed out.

Term.   In algebra a term is a part of an expression which is connected by pluses or minuses with other parts of the expression. In $8xt - mzt^2$, $8xt$ is a term and $-mzt^2$ is a term, and these are the only two terms. The "term in t" is $8xt$, and the "term in t^2" is $-mzt^2$.

Algebraic addition.   When adding expressions in algebra, you can simplify the sum of terms which contain a common factor. For example, you can add $3a$ and $5a$, and obtain an answer $8a$; for example, if a is seven, three sevens and five sevens will add to eight sevens. But to add $3a$ and $7b$, all you can do is put down as an uncondensed result $3a + 7b$. You can also add mp and qp, and arrive at $(m+q)p$.

Algebraic subtraction.   Subtraction may be considered a special case of addition. For subtraction of a positive number is the same as addition of a negative number; and subtraction of a negative number is the same as addition of a positive number. Subtraction of $(a - b + c^2)$ is the same as addition of $(-a + b - c^2)$.

Algebraic Multiplication

In algebra, the process of multiplying single terms is to write them adjacent to each other and simplify. Here are examples:

1) ac times $bd = abcd$

2) $7ab^2c^3$ times $3bc^2d^3 = 21a \cdot b^2 \cdot b \cdot c^3 \cdot c^2 \cdot d^3 = 21ab^3c^5d^3$

To multiply expressions of two or more terms, the following process, very much like arithmetical multiplication, is performed:

$$
\begin{array}{rl}
 & a + b \\
\text{times} & c + d \\
\hline
 & ca + cb \\
 & + da + db \\
\hline
\text{equals} & ac + ad + bc + bd
\end{array}
$$

More examples:

1)
$$a + b$$
times $\quad \underline{a - b}$
$$a^2 + ab$$
$$\underline{\quad - ab - b^2}$$
equals $\quad a^2 - b^2$, since ab and $-ab$ cancel each other out

2)
$$7x + 3y$$
times $\quad \underline{2x + kz}$
equals $\quad \overline{7x \cdot 2x + 3y \cdot 2x}$
$$\underline{\quad\quad + 7x \cdot kz + 3y \cdot kz}$$

which equals $14x^2 + (6y + 7kz)x + 3kyz$; this form of arranging the answer is not covered by a rule but is a matter of choice.

Algebraic Division

Division in algebra has many points of resemblance to division in arithmetic. Here are three examples:

1) Divide $3x^2z$ into $14xy^2z^3$:
$$14xy^2z^3/3x^2z$$
$$= 14/3 \ x^{-1}y^2z^2$$

2) Divide $a + 3$ into $a^2 + 7a + 12$:

$$
\begin{array}{r}
a + 4 \\
a + 3 \overline{) a^2 + 7a + 12} \\
\underline{a^2 + 3a} \\
4a + 12 \\
\underline{4a + 12} \\
0
\end{array}
$$

3) Divide $1 + x + x^2$ into 1:

$$
\begin{array}{r}
1 - x + x^3 - x^4 \ldots \text{ and so on} \\
1 + x + x^2 \overline{) 1} \\
\underline{1 + x + x^2} \\
- x - x^2 \\
\underline{- x - x^2 - x^3} \\
x^3 \\
\underline{x^3 + x^4 + x^5} \\
- x^4 - x^5 \\
\underline{- x^4 - x^5 - x^6} \\
x^6 \ldots \\
\text{and so on}
\end{array}
$$

QUESTION 12: Why not give a set of general rules for division?

Answer: It is possible to state some general rules, but like many of the processes in arithmetic, it is rather easier to look over several examples, see how they behave, and then go and do likewise. This saves the burden of learning a special vocabulary and complicated special rules which are needed in order to state short, exact descriptions of what is happening.

QUESTION 13: I wish you would explain that example (3) to me. If x is 3, for example, then I am trying to divide $1 + x + x^2$, which is $1+3+9$, which is 13, into the dividend 1. My answer should be 1/13. Yet the quotient that appears to be coming is $1 - 3 + 27 - 64$, and so on, and it bounces around and seems to be nowhere near 1/13.

Answer: You have put your finger on a very important point. Often when you are carrying out an operation in algebra that leads to an unending answer (which we have referred to above by the expression "and so on"), the answer that you get is correct for some, but not all, values of the variables, in this case x.

In this case, suppose that x is not 3, but is 1/10. Then the divisor is $1 + \frac{1}{10} + \frac{1}{100}$, which is 1.11. The quotient being produced by the division is now $1 - \frac{1}{10} + \frac{1}{1000} - \frac{1}{10000} \cdots$ "and so on," which is equal to $\frac{9}{10} + \frac{9}{10000} \cdots$ "and so on," which is equal to .9009009 . . . This of course is eminently reasonable, in fact, correct. It can be shown that for x less than 1 the unending expression for the quotient does come closer and closer to the correct answer, and that for x greater than 1, or equal to it, the quotient behaves in a wild way that is not correct.

Factors

One expression is a *factor* of another when the former divides the latter with no remainder. For example:

1) $3a$ is a factor of $12a^3$, for if we divide $3a$ into $12a^3$ we have $4a^2$ as the quotient, and no remainder;

2) $3a$ is also a factor of $14a^4$, for the result of division is $(14/3)a^3$; the fact that the numerical coefficient is a fraction is regularly disregarded in algebra;

3) $x + 2$ is a factor of $x^2 + 5x + 6$, because on dividing we obtain $x + 3$ as the quotient and there is no remainder;

4) But $x + 2$ is not a factor of $x^2 + 6x + 9$, because on division we obtain the quotient $x + 4$ and the remainder of 1 besides.

If one expression exactly divides another, the second is said to be *divisible* by the first.

If we have an algebraic fraction such as $\dfrac{x^2 + 5x + 6}{x^2 + 6x + 8}$, we can, by cancelling the common factors, "reduce it to its lowest terms," a phrase with the same meaning as in arithmetic:

$$\frac{x^2 + 5x + 6}{x^2 + 6x + 8} = \frac{(x + 2)(x + 3)}{(x + 2)(x + 4)} = \frac{x + 3}{x + 4}$$

Equations

One of the important uses of algebra is to solve equations involving numbers that are not known. The simplest algebraic equations are of the form a times x equals b. Here we assume that we know a and b, (which are any given numbers) and we assume that we do not know x and want to find it.

By the use of the axiom about equals, mentioned on page 317, we can solve this equation $ax = b$ with almost no trouble. Divide each side of the equation by a (a not being 0), and we have $x = b/a$.

The equation $ax + b = 0$ can be solved by first subtracting b from both sides, making $ax = -b$, and then dividing both sides by a, so that x is found to be equal to $-b/a$.

This kind of equation is called the *general linear equation with one unknown* or the *general equation of the first degree in one unknown: general* because a and b stand for any numbers in general; *linear* or *first degree* because the only power of the unknown variable x is the first or linear power; *with one unknown* because there is only one unknown variable, x.

For a numerical example, if $7x + 14 = 0$, then a is 7 and b is 14, and using the formula, we have $x = -b/a = -14/7 = -2$. The general equation of the second degree is $ax^2 + bx + c = 0$. This is a much harder equation to solve, but it is still not difficult. It is called the *general quadratic equation in one unknown*. The formula for its solution is $x = \dfrac{-b \pm \sqrt{b^2 - 4ac}}{2a}$ where the sign "$\pm$" means "plus or minus." If we choose the plus sign, we have one value of x which satisfies the equation. If we choose the minus sign, we have another value of x which also satisfies the equation.

For a numerical example, if we have $x^2 + 5x - 6 = 0$, what is x equal to? Substituting in the formula $a = 1$, $b = 5$, $c = -6$, we have:

$$x = \frac{-5 \pm \sqrt{25 + 24}}{2} = \frac{-5 \pm \sqrt{49}}{2} = \frac{-5 \pm 7}{2} = \frac{-5 + 7}{2}, \frac{-5 - 7}{2}$$

$$= +\frac{2}{2}, -\frac{12}{2} = 1, -6$$

Are these two answers, 1 and -6, both correct? Yes. We put 1 into the original equation and we obtain:

$(1)^2 + 5(1) - 6 = 1 + 5 - 6$, which equals 0.

Now we put minus 6 into the original equation, and we obtain:

$(-6)^2 + 5(-6) - 6 = 36 - 30 - 6$, which equals 0.

So both these values of x actually verify in the original equation.

We may easily have equations in two unknowns, such as:

$2x + 3y = 13$

$4x + y = 11$

These are called *linear simultaneous equations in two unknowns: linear* because the highest power of the unknown is the first power; *simultaneous* because we desire to find values of x and y which will satisfy both the equations at the same time; and *with two unknowns* because of course x and y are two and only two unknown variables.

It is possible to solve this pair of equations using the axiom about equals, and using strategy – the strategy of multiplying each equation through by such a number that a later subtraction (of one equation from the other) can make one of the terms vanish.

For example, let us multiply the first equation throughout by 2. We get:

$4x + 6y = 26$

Now write the second equation under it:

$4x + y = 11$

Now subtract the second equation term by term from the first equation: $4x$ from $4x$ gives 0, and the term in x vanishes; $6y$ minus y gives $5y$; and 26 minus 11 gives 15. So we have the equation:

$5y = 15$

Dividing through by 5, we find that y is equal to 3. Since y is equal to 3, we can substitute and change the equation $4x + y = 11$ into $4x + 3 = 11$. Subtracting 3 from both sides, we have $4x$ equals 8. Dividing both sides by 4, we have x equals 2. Our answer is that x equals 2 and y equals 3; these values may be put into the original equations and will verify:

$2(2) + 3(3) = 13$

$4(2) + 3 \quad = 11$

QUESTION 14: Are these all the kinds of equations in algebra, and are they all easy to solve?

Answer: Not by any means. There are a great many kinds of equations in algebra. It is easy to write down examples of equations that would be extremely hard to solve. Here is an example with one unknown.

$$x^7 - ax^4 + b = 0$$

This kind of an equation cannot be solved using what are called elementary methods. In other words, it is not possible to put down a correct *explicit formula* for x.

An explicit formula for x is a formula in which x is on one side of the equals sign by itself, and the known numbers are on the other side of the equals sign by themselves, with accepted algebraic operations being performed on them.

Here is another kind of example impossible to solve neatly and elegantly:

$$3xz + 2x^2y + 8xz^3 = 14$$
$$2xy + 9z^2y + 4zy^4 = 16$$
$$4yz + 7y^3z + 6yz^5 = 18$$

QUESTION 15: How would you solve this set of equations approximately?

Answer: One of the ordinary ways to solve three simultaneous equations as untidy as these would be by a process of intelligent guessing, trying out the guesses, and then modifying the guesses slightly. In this case, one solution is very close to $x = 1$, $y = 1$, and $z = 1$.

It would be very easy to write down equations in algebra which would be almost impossible to solve even by this method. The fact that saves us, however, from monstrosities like these is that there are extremely few situations in the real world out of which equations of this untidy nature actually arise. But that, of course, is an unsatisfactory excuse for a mathematician; it reminds us of Aesop's fable of the fox who could not jump high enough to reach the grapes he wanted, and who, finally giving up, said as he trotted away, "Well, they are sour anyway."

Studying by Yourself

The Objective - Timetable - Getting Started When the Time Comes -
The Organization of Knowledge - Practice in Solving Problems - How
to Make Any Subject Interesting - How to Find Help - The Rewards

IF YOU, the reader of this book, become interested in mathematics, you may think over the possibilities of increasing your knowledge of mathematics and your power to use it, and how useful this will be to you. You may decide that you want to study mathematics. There are two general possibilities. One is to take a mathematics course or class at a nearby school or college. This is a good method, although you may not find just what you would like to learn. The second possibility is studying by yourself. This also is a good method, but it requires a technique.

If you decide that you might be interested in studying by yourself, this appendix is written for you. It attempts to explain some of the techniques of studying any subject by yourself, and to put down some suggestions and experience about what may be called "serious, independent studying." This is the process of attempting to learn some subject by your own efforts week after week, by reading, trying to understand the subject, and thinking about it. It is not easy. But there are rewards, and it is worth considering how to do this kind of studying without too much waste motion, or too much wear and tear upon yourself. For it is one thing for a student to study in school, preparing for regular classes, where many pressures combine to help him study; it is a very different thing to study earnestly outside of school, generating your own pressure for your own studying.

Perhaps no one should say very much about a subject like this unless he has had some experience with it. My main experience consisted of eleven years of studying

evenings and weekends, while holding a full-time job with
frequent overtime. These years were from age 21 to age 32,
when I studied for the actuarial examinations set by the
Society of Actuaries; finally I passed the last one, though for
two of the examinations I had to try four times in four successive years before passing on the fourth try.

If the notes and suggestions in these pages help even a
few students to be successful in their program of studying
by themselves, the notes will have fulfilled their purpose.
But it should be remembered that on the subject of studying,
there are many individual variations among students, and
the last word is never spoken.

The Objective

The objective of your studying should be definite, clear,
and worthwhile. For example, you may say to yourself, "I
really want to know a good deal more about that subject. I
have been interested in it for some time, and it would give
me lasting satisfaction to actually learn something about it."
Or you may say, "It is evident that if I am to make a success
of my occupation, I have to pass those examinations. It may
take me years to do this, but I have got to try. It does not
make sense for me not to try." Or you may say, "This job of
mine requires me to know a good deal more about how this
business operates. I must spend some time finding out more
about it, in order to do my job adequately and advance myself in the business." After you have thought about your
objective, perhaps for weeks or months, and it has become
firm in your mind, then you are ready to study seriously.

It is good sense not to undertake a program of studying
by yourself unless you have a firm conclusion in the back of
your mind, a decision that you have no mental reservations
about. Then you can say peacefully, "I have made up my
mind." You won't have to unmake and remake your decision
time and again as the newness of your effort wears off.

Although the long-term objective may be large, the immediate objective should be neither too large nor too small, taking into account as many factors as you can. Most people who do serious studying at the same time as working at a full-time job find it good to choose an immediate objective that can be worked on from September to May, as in the usual school year, an objective that has a pretty good chance of being accomplished by May. Many sets of professional examinations are organized assuming such a study period.

The objective can usually be stated in a few words; and it is worth writing it down and rereading it from time to time.

Timetable

It is fairly easy to decide on a program of studying by yourself; it is often very hard to stick to it. The spirit may be willing but the flesh is weak.

To make it easier to stick to a program of study, one of the essentials is a timetable. This is a schedule for studying a certain total number of hours a week and a specification, with a little leeway, of the times for study. For example, you may decide: I will study three hours each on Monday, Tuesday, and Thursday evenings, from 7:30 to 10:30, and on Sunday morning and afternoon four hours altogether.

The usual number of hours per week for study should be at least four or five, and may be as high as 20 to 25. Most spare-time students reach the level of 20 or 25 hours a week only in the last few tense weeks before an examination, when they are really caught up in the swing of the studying and are earnestly trying to get through the examination. In the years 1930 to 1941, when I studied for the actuarial examinations, I used to study during the months from September to April. I used to total from 250 to 400 hours of study per season, evenings and weekends — on the average, about 28 weeks of 12 hours of study.

There is no sense in undertaking to study seriously and then not putting in enough time to carry out the objective. How much time is needed? It depends partly on how easily you can learn and remember, partly on how closely the subject is related to your other interests, and on many other factors. But less than four or five hours a week is usually insufficient—you forget from one week to the next just about as much as you learn.

Getting Started When the Time Comes

The biggest problem with any timetable of study is actually starting when the time for starting arrives. I had more trouble with this than with anything else. It was not too hard to stop myself from picking up anything interesting—book, magazine, or whatever—between the time supper ended and the arrival of 7:30. It was not too hard to make myself walk over to my study table or desk and sit down. It was not too hard to know just what subject and what point in the subject I was going ahead with. It was not hard for me to turn off the radio—and there was no television in my day. It was fairly easy to avoid saying yes to invitations on an evening set aside for study.

Nevertheless, it was like pulling teeth for me to get myself started. I would wash my hands, cut my nails, make notes of ideas that I did not want to forget, look over my appointments for the next day, and in many other ways fiddle and doodle. Sometimes 15 minutes or a half hour would go by before I could begin. But once I was started, it was fairly easy to keep on going and to work better and better.

One friend of mine, who is a Fellow of the Society of Actuaries, told me that when he was studying, sometimes the first three hours would count for almost nothing, and then in the fourth hour he would manage to get a good deal done.

Like persuading yourself to jump into cold water, it is a good idea to build up the habit of starting when you have told yourself that you will start. It is like going into cold water, when you count "One — two — and — *three*," and then plunge. I am grateful for the "and," for it gives me one more momentary excuse for not plunging. But when I say "three," I go in. It is a temptation to treat the first count as "just fooling," and try a second count — but that way lies disaster to your willpower.

The Organization of Knowledge

In regard to the content of the knowledge you are studying, it is an interesting fact that all scientific subjects and a great many others (excluding astrology, fortunetelling, magic, and other branches of nonsense) are organized essentially in the same simple way: in terms of sensible ideas and consistent relations between them. So your problem of studying breaks down into the following steps:

1) *Ideas.* You identify the ideas peculiar to the subject. In other words, you find out the meaning of the terms and expressions peculiar to the subject.

2) *Relations.* You also find out the relations that associate the ideas, the kinds of statements that associate the terms and expressions of the subject.

3) *Memorizing.* You do at least some memorizing, committing to your memory the most essential ideas so that you can recall them when you want to use them.

4) *Problem-Solving.* You practice answering questions, working out solutions to problems, so that you practice using the new ideas. In fact, there is little sense in learning a lot of ideas without learning how to apply them, how to use them in situations. For example, the finest definition of probability is not worth much unless you learn also how to apply it in simple chance situations, like figuring out how often three coins when tossed will all come up heads.

Because of these steps, part of studying any subject necessarily consists of making a careful digest or glossary of what appear to be all the important ideas in a subject—the terms and the relations between them. This you should make for yourself, by writing or typing or speaking, or in some other way, so that when you need to use the information, you have already given it expression at least once—as writing performed by your own fingers, or words spoken by your own voice.

Practice in Solving Problems

Knowledge is not really learned unless it can be used. For this reason, anyone who is studying a subject needs to do work on problems and to practice producing the solutions to them.

For each subdivision of a subject, it is a good idea to select from the references a number of problems. This number should vary from three or four up to 30 or 40, depending on the dimensions of the subdivision of the subject, the variety of common problems, whether you can do them easily or not, and other factors. Then you should try to work out the problems, one by one, proceeding from the simpler ones to the more complicated, and aiming to solve some of each of the common types.

As you finish a problem, you should seek to verify your answer. In the case of mathematical problems, one good way is to substitute your answer into the conditions of the problem and see if it verifies. Another good way is to put numbers in the place of variables and see if the starting expression and the finishing expression give the same numbers. If they do, there is a good chance (though not a complete proof) that your answer is right.

A final, useful test of your command of the subject is to see if you can construct problems that are interesting and of the same general type as the problems in the references, and then solve these also correctly and easily.

How to Make Any Subject Interesting

People find it easy to work on things that are interesting. If we can succeed in making something that we want to study interesting, it will be easy for us to study it.

When is something interesting? It is interesting when it stimulates your curiosity, when you eagerly desire to know the answer to some question about it. When you are reading a novel and become curious about what will happen to the characters, the story is hard to put down. When you have a headache that won't go away, it occupies your attention, you want fiercely to find some medicine or some behavior that will make your headache go away—you become interested in your headache.

In mathematics, one of the numbers that often turns up is pi, 3.14159265 . . . Why does it turn up so often? Is it necessary that the circumference of every circle be exactly pi times its diameter? Why? How do people know what the digits in pi are? What is a good way to calculate pi to a number of decimals? Mathematicians say that the digits in pi never repeat, as they do for example in the decimal form of 2/11, which equals .1818181818 . . . with 18 recurring forever. But why don't the digits in pi repeat in cycles? How can this be proved?

In a few minutes you can ask enough meaningful questions about pi to have your curiosity stimulated for the rest of your life. In fact, there is much interesting history in the answering of these questions; and often the guessed answer and the proof of the guess are as much as 200 years apart.

Why are people curious? People, especially young people, are endowed with an instinct that makes them cruious, inquisitive, about the world and all the things in it. This instinct, this inherited tendency, is one of the important characteristics of human beings, and one of their glories. Curiosity is at the base of culture, civilization, and science. Take fire, for example. If man were no more curious about fire than a dog is, he would never have learned to master it. So, all we need to do to become curious about a lot of things is simply to let our instinct of curiosity become stirred up by asking questions.

In fact, for almost any idea, we can ask questions that will make it interesting. Here are a few of the questions:

What is its name? What are other names for it?
What are some examples of it?
How is it defined?
What is its essence, its kernel?
What is it like? What is it related to?
What is it different from? What is it opposite to?
What is its genus, what kind of thing is it?
What are its properties? Its characteristics?
How is it used?
Why is it important?
What is its origin?
What will it develop into?
How can it be of use to me?

How to Find Help

After you have begun to work on your study program and have found out some things about the beginning of your subject, you will find questions that are not easily answered from whatever books you are reading. In order to get those questions answered, you have several resources. One resource consists of friends or associates who might know the answers; if you ask an intelligent question of the right person at the right time, he is usually delighted to try to explain the answer to you. Another resource consists of books by other authors on the same subject; where different authors disagree, you yourself may have an opinion that is just as good as any of theirs. A third resource consists of inquiries to authorities—you either write them or seek them out and talk to them. Sometimes this is your only resource:

if you should find a clear, eight-sided stone, with triangles for the sides, bright and very hard, perhaps the only way to be sure what kind of stone it is would be to take it to a mineralogist or geologist and ask, "What is this?"

Often you cannot get a satisfying answer even with a reasonable amount of effort. Then the best thing to do is to mark the question in your mind as either unanswered or answered tentatively, and go ahead in the most reasonable way you can. In fact, much information is uncertain; and much information believed today will be proved wrong in the years to come. Many scientists live with unanswered questions and uncertain information all their lives.

The Rewards

The rewards for completing a program of serious study by yourself are great. You prove to yourself and to your associates that you are able to learn information to advance yourself. You have demonstrated your perseverance. You amount to more as a person and you increase your confidence in your abilities. You use the information learned to make wiser choices at many times in the future, with all the good that this brings.

And finally and perhaps most important, you take into your own life the knowledge that countless other human beings have worked years and years to discover, put together, and establish. You come into your inheritance from the ages.

A Short Bibliography

AT LEAST A HUNDRED GOOD BOOKS have been written on mathematics for persons who are not mathematicians. Some of these deal mainly with mathematical recreations. Others deal with the history of mathematics and the role of mathematics in society. A few meet all of the following requirements:

- They are well-suited to persons who are not mathematicians;
- They actually instruct in some useful mathematics;
- They are interesting, generally understandable, and often fascinating.

The following six books, I think, meet all these requirements.

The first four books do not require much work. The fifth one does — it requires a good deal of patient study. And the sixth one is more for reference than for reading. These six books are the ones I would select for a nonmathematician to take with him to a desert island, if one of the requirements for survival on the island were a reasonable knowledge of mathematics!

Davis, Philip J., *The Lore of Large Numbers*, No. 6 in the New Mathematical Library, Monograph Project of the School Mathematics Study Group headquartered at Yale University. Random House, Inc., 457 Madison Ave., New York, N.Y., 10020, 1961. Paperback, 165 pp.

> This book is full of amusing examples and interesting and worthwhile information about large numbers and related ideas. The author says "by means of approximate computation and estimation, I have suggested that numbers may be handled lightly and efficiently as friends with whom one discourses, rather than as enemies against whom one struggles." Some of the chapters are: "How Large Is Large?"; "Division by Zero —

the Road to Paradox"; "The Long Long Trail of Pi." Pages 130 to 135 contain an appendix "Some Selected Magnitudes in Science and Mathematics" and provide a very good base for making estimates. About 25 references are given in the bibliography.

Sawyer, W. W., *Mathematician's Delight* (8th edition). Penguin Books, 3300 Clipper Mill Road, Baltimore 11, Md., 1956. Paperback, 238 pp.

This book provides an introduction to mathematics. The author's first sentence is "The main object of this book is to dispel the fear of mathematics." Some of the chapters are: "The Dread of Mathematics"; "The Nature of Reasoning"; "How to Forget the Multiplication Table"; "Trigonometry, or How to Make Tunnels and Maps." No bibliography.

Bross, Irwin D. J., *Design for Decision*. The Macmillan Co., 60 Fifth Ave., New York, N.Y. 10011, 1953. 276 pp.

This is an illuminating introduction to the ideas of statistics for the purpose of making decisions based on statistical evidence. It contains many amusing and informative examples. The author says: "Statistical Decision can be viewed as a complex machine. Into this machine is fed information about the real world, and out of this machine comes a recommendation for action in the real world." Some of the chapters are: "History of Decision"; "Operating a Decision-Maker"; "Sampling"; "Statistical Inference." The book contains a list of 38 references recommended for further reading.

Kasner, Edward, and Newman, James R., *Mathematics and the Imagination*. Simon and Schuster, 630 Fifth Ave., New York, N.Y. 10020, 1940. 380 pp.

This is a book sparkling with wit and good examples. It seeks to make many of the ideas of mathematics accessible and attractive to the nonmathematician. In this book the word "googol" was coined. The authors seek to show "something of the character of mathematics, of its bold, untrammeled spirit, of how as both an art and a science it has continued to lead the

creative faculties beyond even imagination and intuition."
Some of the chapters are: "Beyond the Googol"; "Rubber-
Sheet Geometry"; "Change and Changeability." About 40
references are given in the bibliography.

Courant, Richard, and Robbins, Herbert, *What Is Mathematics? An Elementary Approach to Ideas and Methods*
(4th edition). Oxford University Press, 417 Fifth Ave., New
York, N.Y., 1948. 521 pp.

> This is a jewel of a book. It is a fine, carefully written intro-
> duction to mathematics, presupposing only high school mathe-
> matics — but it requires study and effort. It gives a genuine
> understanding of mathematical concepts. The authors say:
> "Knowledge cannot be attained by indirect means alone. . . .
> Understanding of mathematics cannot be transmitted by pain-
> less entertainment. . . . Actual contact with the content of living
> mathematics is necessary. . . . Technicalities and detours should
> be avoided. . . . It is possible to proceed on a straight road from
> the very elements to vantage points from which the substance
> and driving forces of modern mathematics can be surveyed. . . .
> This book is an attempt in this direction." And, let it be said,
> a very good attempt. Among the topics mentioned are: "The
> Principle of Mathematical Induction"; "The Mathematical
> Analysis of Infinity"; "Impossibility Proofs in Geometry"; "The
> Technique of Finding Derivatives." About 70 references are
> given in the bibliography.

Karush, William, *The Crescent Dictionary of Mathematics.*
The Macmillan Co., 60 Fifth Ave., New York, N.Y. 10011,
1962. Photo offset, 313 pp.

> This is an excellent dictionary and short encyclopedia of
> some 1,400 mathematical ideas of standard high school and
> college mathematics. The author says, "The dictionary is in-
> tended for several audiences: participants in high school and
> college mathematics — the student and the teacher . . . many
> professional workers in the behavioral and social sciences . . .
> the general reader with an intellectual interest in mathe-
> matics. . . . The explanations of entries range from brief defini-
> tions of a few lines to expository discussions of various lengths."
> Over 70 references are given in the bibliography.

The following works are mentioned in the text:

Boole, George, *An Investigation of the Laws of Thought.* Walton and Maberley, London, 1854, reprinted by Dover Publications, New York, N.Y. 424 pp.

Etzioni, Amitai, *The Hard Way to Peace.* Collier Books, New York, N.Y., 1962. Paperbound, 285 pp.

Heath, T. L., *The Thirteen Books of Euclid's Elements.* Cambridge, England, 1908.

Hilton, James, *Lost Horizon.* William Morrow and Co., Inc. New York, N.Y., 1933, reprinted by Pocket Books, New York, N.Y.

Miller, George A., *Language and Communication.* McGraw-Hill Book Co., New York, 1951. 298 pp.

Onions, C. T., editor, *The Shorter Oxford English Dictionary on Historical Principles.* 3rd edition, 2 volumes. The Clarendon Press, Oxford, 1944. 2,494 pp.

Rickover, H. G., *Education and Freedom.* E. P. Dutton & Co., Inc., New York, N.Y., 1959. 256 pp.

Computers and Automation (monthly magazine). Berkeley Enterprises, Inc., Newtonville, Mass. 1951 to date.

INDEX

This index contains not only the expected mathematical entries but also references to the many examples — natural phenomena, games, puzzles, ordinary everyday situations, flora and fauna, characters real and imaginary — used by the author to explain and enliven the mathematical concepts treated in the book.

———————————— HOW TO . . . ————————————

──────────── SIGNS AND NUMERALS ────────────